D1286501

THE WORLD'S TANKERS

Laurence Dunn

THE WORLD'S TANKERS

ADLARD COLES LIMITED
in association with
GEORGE G. HARRAP AND COMPANY LIMITED
London · Toronto · Sydney · Wellington
and
JOHN DE GRAFF INC. · *New York*

Books by the same Author

SHIP RECOGNITION: MERCHANT SHIPS
SHIP RECOGNITION: WARSHIPS
LINERS AND THEIR RECOGNITION
SHIPS OF THE UNION CASTLE LINE
SHIPS OF SOUTHAMPTON

FIRST PUBLISHED 1956
COPYRIGHT IN ALL COUNTRIES SIGNATORY TO THE BERNE CONVENTION

Printed in Great Britain by
SYDENHAM & CO. (EST. 1840) LTD., BOURNEMOUTH

Introduction

IN just under a century the production of petroleum and its derivatives has risen from insignificance to become one of the world's greatest industries. Originally the main needs were for illuminating and lubricating oils, and progress was gradual. However, towards the end of the nineteenth century there came the development of the internal combustion engine, and with this the tremendous expansion of the oil industry really began.

The first well to be specifically drilled for oil was sunk in 1859 and in that year the world's total production was about 1,000 tons. So small was the demand for the outpourings of this and other early wells that oil flowed away unwanted, choking nearby rivers and creeks, while such as could be sold fetched only two cents per barrel. Today the world's annual output has reached astronomical proportions, around five hundred million tons.

Parallel with the need for liquid fuels has been the demand for ships to transport them, and the tanker has developed from a vessel of small size and often crude design into one of the best equipped and highly evolved types of merchant ship afloat. In the early years the oil-carrier was of ill repute, and crews could only be found with difficulty. Inevitably the tanker of today spends a far greater proportion of her life at sea than does the dry cargo carrier, while loading and discharge—normally a matter of hours—is generally done at some out of the way point where there are no shore amenities. But these factors are more than offset by the very high standard of accommodation provided for the tanker crews, who also receive an extra generous amount of leave.

In this book I have endeavoured to record the development of the oil tanker, and the early gropings for an efficient and practical design: to describe some of the strange ships which resulted from the conflict of opinion among designers, and the eventual emergence of the form which served as the basis of tanker design today. Then to show the steady growth through the years, both in peace and war, also the types favoured by the various nations and for individual trades: finally, the coming of the giant tankers, which in dimensions if not in gross tonnage closely rival the *Queen Elizabeth* herself.

For many years Norway has been regarded as the home of the independently owned tanker and at the close of 1955 her tanker fleet was the second largest in the world. But one of the most notable new developments has been the entry of Greek owners into this business. In the course of one decade they have built up a tanker fleet outstanding for its design and also for the size and speed of many of its individual units.

A final word concerning the illustrations in this book. In theory the photographs chosen should only be of the highest pictorial quality. In many cases, however, it has been impossible to achieve this standard, especially with regard to bygone vessels. In order to portray tanker development as fully as possible, I have therefore had to include some which are justified only by their technical or historical interest. Here I beg the reader's indulgence.

LAURENCE DUNN

1st January, 1956.

Contents

Illustrations

8

ILLUSTRATIONS (*continued*)

ILLUSTRATIONS (*continued*)

ILLUSTRATIONS (*continued*)

Evolution of Hull Shapes

THIS initial section has been prepared to help give an idea of the development of the tanker as regards size and shape, and also of the relationship between length and tonnage, a point impossible to appreciate by photographs alone. Then to show, by a series of cross sections, the most favoured cargo tank arrangements. Finally, to illustrate a few stages in the development of the bridge; how it has grown from a low structure providing the minimum of protection and no comfort into the present-day citadel, containing the most modern and comprehensive array of navigational aids and, on the decks below, excellent accommodation for captain, officers and sometimes passengers.

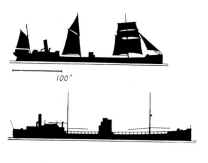

100'

Tonnage-Length Comparisons

3,000 tons d.w., 2,307 tons gross. 310 ft. overall. *Gluckauf*, 1886. British built, German owned. The prototype of the present-day tanker.

6,800 tons d.w., 5,069 tons gross. 367 ft. overall. *Hamlet*, 1915. The first Norwegian motor tanker. Swedish built.

12,500 tons d.w., 8,552 tons gross. 486 ft. overall. *British Caution*, 1946. British built and owned. One of very large size group.

24,500 tons d.w., 16,145 tons gross. 611 ft. overall. *Oceanus*, 1954. Swedish built and owned. The first large tanker with bridge aft.

38,900 tons d.w., 22,610 tons gross. 707 ft. overall. *Liberty Bell*, 1954. Built and owned in U.S.A. One of four, the fastest and most powerful super-tankers to date.

47,750 tons d.w., over 30,000 tons gross. 757 ft. overall. *Spyros Niarchos*, 1956. British built, Greek owned. The world's largest to date.

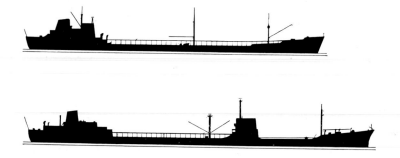

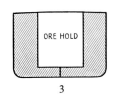
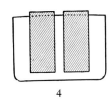

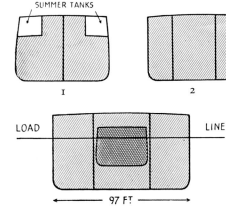

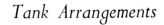

LOAD   LINE

97 FT

5

Tank Arrangements

1. The summer tank arrangement was standard for many years. So-called summer tanks met expansion needs, or on occasion could be used to carry light oils. Still used in molasses carriers.

2. The present arrangement, in which two longitudinal bulkheads form three sets of tanks.

3. The combined oil/ore ship carries oil in L-shaped tanks either side and under the ore space.

4. The chemical carrier, of which there are many variations. The cylinders, either two or three abreast, are generally arranged vertically.

5. A size contrast provided by the early *Gluckauf* (1886) and the *Spyros Niarchos* which carries a deadweight of 47,750 tons. Draught having reached its maximum, the result is the building of more beamy vessels.

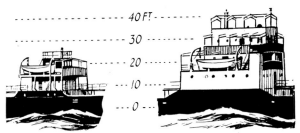

The Development
of the Bridge

Above left: Typical low open bridge of the late 'nineties. Note very small wheelhouse. Size of ship about 5,000 tons d.w.

Above right: Angular solid based bridge, popular during the 'twenties. Size of ship usually 10,000 tons d.w. Note double awning ridges.

Left: The massive streamlined bridge of the *Spyros Niarchos*, 47,750 tons d.w. Completed 1956. Unlike the other two, it is not built on an 'island,' but rises from the main deck. Note stanchions slope in harmony with each other and with the after edge of mast and bridge.

Note no gangway forward.

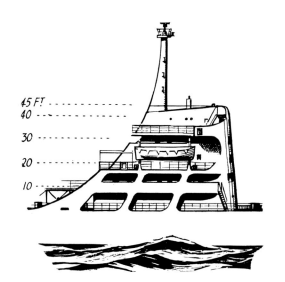

Sectional drawing of the super-tanker *Spyros Niarchos*, 47,750 tons d.w., built by Vickers-Armstrongs for the Niarchos Group. Length o.a. 757 ft., breadth 97 ft. 4 in., draught 37 ft. 10½ in. Starting forward there is a dry cargo hold; next a cofferdam, then eleven triple cargo tanks. Another cofferdam aft separates these from oil bunker tanks which flank a centreline pump room. Further aft are the boiler and engine rooms.

A CONTRAST IN BRIDGE SHAPES

The elaborate structure of the s.s. *British Soldier* (21,082 tons gross), one of a class of six ships, each of 32,000 tons d.w., which are owned by the British Tanker Co. Ltd.

LAURENCE DUNN

Above the latter are large fuel tanks, with smaller fresh water tanks in the engineers' workshop. On the next two decks above are the crew's quarters and some of the officers' accommodation. Above again (in front of the funnel) is the chief engineer's suite and (aft) the hospital. The captain's quarters are shown under the navigating bridge; beneath are the owner's rooms, then the deck officers' accommodation.

The austere, streamlined bridgehouse of the s.s. *Phoenix* (25,733 tons gross). This vessel has a d.w. tonnage of 44,633 and is one of the largest tankers in the world. She was built in Japan, 1954, for the Universe Tankships Inc.

Acknowledgments

LOOKING BACK through this book's progress to the time when it was little more than an idea, the most remarkable aspect which emerges is that of the generous assistance given me by those in the oil industry and many others; without whom collectively, the final work would hardly have been possible.

In particular I should like to express my sincere thanks to the following: The Chief of Naval Information, Admiralty, American Oil Co., Athel Line Ltd., Bethlehem Steel Co., Shipbuilding Division, British Tanker Co. Ltd., Caltex Trading & Transport Co. Ltd., Cities Service Oil Co., Eagle Oil & Shipping Co. Ltd., Esso Petroleum Co. Ltd., Gotaverken A/B, Harland & Wolff Ltd., *Holland Shipbuilding & Marine Engineering*, Hunting & Son Ltd., John I. Jacobs & Co. Ltd., Kockums Mek. Verkstads A/B, Lloyd's Register of Shipping, London & Overseas Freighters Ltd., Percival Marshall & Co. Ltd., Niarchos (London) Ltd., Regent Oil Co. Ltd., Shell, Shell-Mex & B.P. Ltd., *The Shipping World*, *Syren & Shipping*, John I. Thornycroft & Co. Ltd., Trinidad Leaseholds Ltd., the U.S. Navy, and the official photographers of the shipowners and shipbuilders concerned.

Photographs which deserve special mention are those used for the jacket ("The tanker *Gretafield* in heavy weather"), end papers and frontispiece. For these respectively I am indebted to Hunting & Son Ltd., the Shell Photo Unit and the Bethlehem Steel Co., Shipbuilding Division.

Also I thank J. R. Richardson, Esq., who so kindly read the proofs of this book, and W. H. Brown, Esq., Jeffery Curtis, Esq., A. R. Huggett, Esq., John Lamb, Esq., O.B.E., and R. M. Scott, Esq.

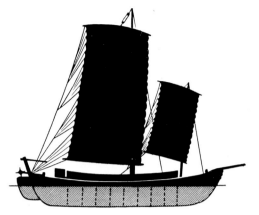

Eighteenth century. A Newchwang junk
used for carrying oil in the eighteenth
century. About 55 ft. in length, these junks
had a capacity of about 50 tons.

1

The First Oil Ships

IT is impossible to say precisely when oil was first transported at sea, but
certainly as far back as A.D. 670 Greek fireships carried a certain amount of
petroleum in bulk as part of their offensive equipment. Of commercial bulk
oil carriers the Newchwang junks were probably the oldest. These craft had
for a very long time been engaged in transporting salt water in bulk up the
Chinese rivers to the saltpans and others in carrying live fish when, in the
early part of the eighteenth century, some were modified to carry bean oil
in bulk. A typical example of these junks measured approximately 55 ft. in
length by 13 ft. in beam and could carry some 50 tons of oil. As in more
recent designs, the cargo space was divided by transverse bulkheads and
provided with a trunk for the expansion and contraction of cargo.

Another very early trade concerned the transportation of petroleum by
native sailing craft down the Irrawaddy to Rangoon where it was refined.

In the early eighteenth century oil collected near Baku was being carried in bulk by Iranian river craft. Even then this trade, according to a visitor there, was regarded as being a very old one. It was on the Volga, however, that the greatest activity occurred and here from 1725 onwards the carriage of oil in bulk had to conform to regulations issued by Peter the Great.

About a hundred years ago the shale oil industry in Great Britain and that of mineral oil in America started simultaneously to meet a need of the times. For by the late 'fifties the whaling industry was on the decline, whales becoming so scarce that the profit in pursuing them was dubious. The world was being ransacked for other animal and vegetable fats while operators of machinery had the very real fear of a world famine of lubricating oils.

The famous oil well at Titusville was drilled by Colonel Drake in 1859 and inaugurated a new and far cheaper source of supply of both lubricants and illuminants. The ocean transport of oil began very unobtrusively a year later when an enterprising Pittsburger brought American petroleum in homeopathic quantities to Britain. Almost immediately Philadelphia became the premier port as regards the transit of oil to the United Kingdom. At first a few sample barrels were shipped in general cargo vessels, but in November, 1861, Messrs. Peter Wright & Sons, of Philadelphia chartered the brig *Elizabeth Watts*, 224 tons, to load a cargo of oil in barrels for London. Very little is known about the trip. So dangerous was her cargo considered that when she was ready for sea her captain was only able to obtain a crew by enlisting the aid of crimps and it was with a drunken crew that she finally sailed down the Delaware River. However, the *Elizabeth Watts* crossed the Atlantic in safety and landed her cargo in good condition at a London wharf.

This successful voyage led to others and by 1864 the year's exports of petroleum from the Philadelphia was 7,600,000 gallons, the total for the whole of the States being 31,750,000 gallons. Mr. Henry Duncan of Bromley, Kent, claimed to have sent the first oil carrying vessel to Europe by way of the Canadian canals and the St. Lawrence River. In 1863 he bought a schooner at Chicago, loaded her with petroleum at Sarnia and despatched her to Liverpool. That she was lost in the Gulf of St. Lawrence

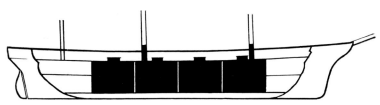

1863. The *Atlantic*, built of iron in 1863, was designed for trans-Atlantic trade. She had four tanks, and two of her masts served as expansion trunks. She was wrecked after a life of only six years.

before she had reached the Atlantic does not detract from his claim to have been the pioneer of American interlake and ocean navigation.

Early that year (1863) an Isle of Man shipowner built the *Ramsay*, an iron hulled sailing tanker. Her cargo space was subdivided by a centreline and several thwartships bulkheads and had a capacity of some 1,400 tons of petroleum. She was fitted with a patent cargo expansion device. The tanks which were airtight were equipped with a siphon, of which one end dipped into water carried in an adjacent tank. Expansion of the oil caused this to exert pressure on the water, some of which was forced up the tube. Neither vapour or oil could escape, and in contraction the water level returned to normal.

Another noteworthy ship of 1863 was the *Atlantic*, a small iron built sailing vessel, which was launched on August 1st from Rogerson's shipyard at St. Peter's, the Tyneside birthplace of many collier brigs. Fitted to carry petroleum in bulk 'without the aid of casks,' she was designed for the Atlantic oil trade which was then beginning to arouse the interest of a number of shipowners in the North of England. She, like the *Great Western*, which was built there a little later, had her tank space subdivided by a central longitudinal and three transverse bulkheads, making eight in all. Expansion of cargo was provided for by the fitting of hollow iron masts. These two ships were the first to carry their own cargo pumps. The *Atlantic* had a short life, being wrecked about six years later, but the *Great Western* operated until the 'nineties.

The *Charles,* another of the pioneer sailing vessels built to carry petroleum in iron tanks, was employed from 1869 to 1872 in transporting crude oil between the United States and Europe. She had a capacity of 794 tons and carried her liquid cargo in tanks—59 in all—arranged along the bottom of her holds and in the 'tween decks. These were worked on the separate tank system, there being no pipe connections. Nor were there any arrangements for keeping the tanks full. Tanks found to be leaking during the voyage were topped up with salt water.

Each year up to 1878 wooden sailers were adapted to carry oil in bulk, the holds themselves forming the tanks. Occasionally, too, a steamer crossed the Atlantic with barrelled oil. These tank sailers gradually wiped out the barrel carrying sailers, as being larger and more economical they could offer lower rates of freight. At that time it was estimated that a barrel weighed 64 lb. or one-fifth of the weight of the oil it contained. Added to this was the waste of hold space. A ship with a dry cargo capacity of 2,000 tons could only lift 1,030 tons of barrelled oil. There was, too, the added cost of labour and the loss on the sale of the barrels themselves, which might amount to as much as £350/£475 per voyage on a ship of this size.

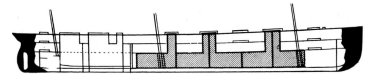

1872. The Belgian s.s. *Vaderland* of the Red Star Line was the first steamer designed to carry petroleum in bulk; there are, however, no records of her being used for this. Built at Jarrow in 1872, she measured 320 ft. in length. Her engines were placed aft, and her passenger accommodation flanked the expansion trunks.

The first ocean-going tank steamer to be built was *Vaderland* of 1872, the pioneer of the Red Star Line. This company, which received a subsidy from the Belgian Government, conceived the ingenious idea of building ships which could carry passengers to the States and return to Europe with bulk cargoes of petroleum. Not unnaturally the authorities decided that such a scheme was far too dangerous and the idea of carrying oil had to be dropped before a passenger certificate was granted. The *Vaderland*, which was built by Palmers, of Jarrow, had a gross tonnage of 2,748 and measured 320 ft. in length by 38 ft. breadth. She had three masts and her engines placed aft. The first of a trio to be built at this yard, she was followed in 1873 and 1874 by the generally similar *Nederland* and *Switzerland*, which, however, had their machinery amidships. In all three there was a space of about two feet between the sides of the tanks and the hull itself. The expansion trunks, which reached to the upper deck, were flanked each side by the passenger accommodation. Dry cargo was subsequently carried in these tanks but their shape prevented easy stowage. Interesting though these three ships were, they contributed little or nothing to the development of tanker design.

In September, 1879, when some forty European ports were receiving refined oil from the United States, the Norwegians started a new phase by sending their first tanker, the *Stat*, to Philadelphia to load a cargo of crude oil in bulk. On October 18th she left that port for Rouen with the first cargo of petroleum ever loaded in an eastbound tank steamer. Within a week two more Norwegian vessels arrived at Philadelphia: these were the oil sailer *Lindenoer* and the brig *Jan Mayn*, which were fitted out in the same manner as the *Stat* and, like her, loaded for Rouen. Their success inspired a French venture, but their tank ship, the *Fanny*, mysteriously disappeared on her first voyage, while bound for Havre with a cargo of crude.

Prominent among German owners of the 'seventies was Heinrich Riedemann, who had a number of case-oil carrying sailing ships. Two vessels which he subsequently bought for the emigrant trade were equipped with very large tanks for the carriage of drinking water. However, as their crews much preferred to have their water from casks, he used these tanks for oil. The results were so satisfactory that he began to think of carrying bulk oil in this fashion.

Meanwhile in the Caspian region great developments had been taking place, largely due to the genius of two Swedish men. These were Robert and Ludwig Nobel, brothers of Alfred Nobel of explosives fame. After first using wooden barges for the carriage of oil residium they conceived the idea of transporting refined products in barges and sailing vessels fitted with iron tanks or holds lined with cement. Originally their fleet operated from Baku to the mouth of the Volga, but later they continued up the various rivers.

Their *Zoroaster* which came out in 1878 was notable as being the first tank steamer to be actually used as such. Built in Sweden by the Lindholmen Motala yard, she had engines amidships, *burned oil fuel* and originally carried her cargoes of kerosene—about 250 tons—in 21 vertical cylindrical tanks. These, however, were later removed, the cargo being carried next the skin. She was followed soon after by more ambitious vessels fitted with their engines aft. These were the *Budah, Nordenskiold* and *Moses*, the first two of which had four longitudinal bulkheads besides the usual thwartships ones, and unlike the *Zoroaster* were fitted with expansion tanks.

Within four years of the delivery of the *Zoroaster*, the Nobel Brothers' fleet had grown to include a dozen tank steamers designed for service on the Caspian as well as an equal number of shallow draught tank barges operating on the Volga. The former operated from Baku to the mouth of the Volga and back, the round trip taking about six days. The largest of these ships had a capacity of about 800 tons.

A notable trio ordered by Russians from the Armstrong Mitchell yard were the *Massis*, *Poseidon* and *Armeniak*. These, too, were for the Caspian trade. Three-masted ships with engines aft, they were completed about 1883. The first-named was primarily a case oil carrier, but had a 70-ton oil tank amidships.

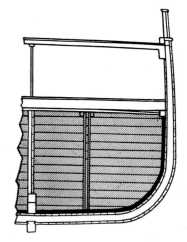

Another interesting idea was applied to the *Crusader*, an elderly wooden barque which was fitted with three tiers of cylindrical tanks — 47 in all—which were placed in horizontal position four abreast. Each cylinder or tank had its own independent piping which was led to the hatch above and then to flexible hoses, which were used for loading and discharge. The cargo was handled by an 8 h.p. pumping engine which was fitted on deck. Another pipe system led to a pressure tank which provided overflow space during expansion or, alternatively, offset any leakage.

1878. Half section of a typical wooden sailing ship designed to carry oil in bulk, and built about 1878. Surge of the liquid cargo was reduced by the fitting of fore and aft washboards approximately midway between the centreline bulkhead and the sides of the hull, which were lined with either cement or felt.

Impressed by the idea, Heinrich Riedemann of the Deutsche-Amerikanische Petroleum Gesselschaft converted the sailer *Andromeda*, but in a much more elaborate manner, building 72 steel tanks which became an integral part of the structure. These held a total of 3,000 tons and were arranged 24 on each of the three decks, either side of central fore and aft passages. Expansion and cargo handling arrangements were greatly improved. There was a main filling pipe running fore and aft, while each tank had 3-inch pipe connections, as well as air and sounding pipes.

2

Pioneer Tankers

DURING the early 'eighties many sailing vessels were converted into oil carriers and though these were constantly employed in the Atlantic trade they could only provide very irregular deliveries. At this time there was great discussion as to whether tanks should be kept clear of the hull itself, or if the latter should form part of the tank sides. It was not until about 1884 that the latter became widely accepted as practicable. The next few years—up to about 1890 or so—were the critical ones as regards tanker design. Experience gained from early experimental craft was accumulating to form a background of knowledge from which more advanced designs could be evolved.

In January, 1885, it was announced that the Black Sea Steam Navigation Co. (a Nobel concern) had ordered the building of a fleet of steamers from British and Swedish shipyards. Each was to be fitted with petroleum tanks and have a capacity of 1,500 tons, the idea being to compete with the Americans in the supply of oil to Europe. Later that year a tank steamer of greatly improved design was delivered by the Swedish Lindholmen yard to a rival concern, the Russian Steam Navigation & Trading Co., of Odessa. The *Sviet*, as she was named, had a gross tonnage of 1,827, measured 273.9 ft. in length by 35.1 ft. in breadth and had a speed of 11 knots. She had machinery and boilers aft, with a cofferdam separating these from the tank space. The pump room was placed right forward, while the rest of the ship—about half her length—was devoted to tank space. One longitudinal and five transverse bulkheads were fitted, and these provided four pairs of tanks which, however, did not extend to the hull itself. At the sides they finished nearly two feet short of the outer skin. Above there was a clearance of inches only, while beneath was a cellular bottom.

About that time a representative of Nobel Brothers, of Antwerp, was in England offering a five-year charter to carry oil from Batum. This was accepted by a Middlesbrough firm of shipowners, John M. Lennard & Sons. As there was no time to build a new ship, an existing one, the s.s. *Fergusons* (1,504 tons gross) was taken in hand and converted by Craggs & Co., who had a shipbuilding yard in the same town. A number of iron tanks were built separately and then lifted aboard. Specially shaped to fit the hull, the lower pairs stowed snugly into the holds and the upper ones into the 'tween decks. To keep these tanks full and prevent surge, other 'regulating' tanks were also fitted in the 'tween decks. Reasonably successful in operation, the *Fergusons* had but a short life, being destroyed by an explosion at Rouen in 1889.

It was a Russian steamer the *Petrolea* (later *Ludwig Nobel*) which about a year or so later (the exact date is uncertain) brought the first cargo of bulk oil to the Thames. The ship berthed at the Regent's Canal Dock and discharged her 1,000-ton cargo—from Libau—into tanks at Atlantic Wharf, Bow, after pipelines had been laid beneath the streets. Her cargo, which was handled by Lane & MacAndrew, of London, was quickly sold, for at the time oil stocks were low owing to many oil sailers being held up in the Channel by adverse winds. This started a long connection between Lane & MacAndrew and the Russian oil trade. Subsequently this firm owned a large fleet of tank steamers.

Two other notable conversions from dry cargo steamers occurred in 1886, these being the *Chigwell* and *Petriana* for Alfred Suart, a man who had a rather meteoric career and did much to develop the tanker business in Britain. The *Chigwell*, then three years old, was a ship of 1,824 tons gross and measured 258.8 ft. in length. She was given four tanks forward and three aft, and fitted with a fore and aft centreline bulkhead. She differed from the *Fergusons* in that her cargo was carried next the sides and top of the hull. The *Chigwell* was later bought by the Shell Transport & Trading Co. Ltd., and operated successfully for many years.

A much more important event, however, was the building of the

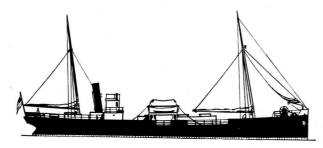

The first U.S. Pacific coastal tanker, the *George Loomis* was built by the Union Iron Works, Richmond, Cal., a company later bought by the Bethlehem Pacific Coast Steel Corporation. She had a d.w. capacity of 800 tons, and her cargo space was divided by one longitudinal and two transverse bulkheads. Owners: Pacific Coast Oil Co. Length 175.0 ft., breadth 27.4 ft. This profile shows her original appearance. Compare with illustration on facing page.

Gluckauf. Encouraged by the success of their *Crusader,* the German-American Petroleum Company decided to build a tank steamer that was specially designed as such. Only the firm of Armstrong Mitchell & Co., of Newcastle, would consider their proposals and the ship was accordingly built at their yard, to the design of Colonel Henry F. Swan. The *Gluckauf* has a unique position in the history of tanker development, being regarded as the prototype of all existing vessels of this type. She incorporated the best of the ideas found in earlier experimental tankers and many that were quite new. As the illustration shows, she had engines aft, a long poop and short fo'c'sle. The bridge—a very small structure—was amidships, making the forward well a very long one. She measured 300.5 ft. in length, 37.2 ft. in breadth and had a gross tonnage of 2,307. Oil was carried next the skin of the ship and to avoid the accumulation of dangerous gases the double bottom was eliminated except under the engine room. She had the usual fore and aft centreline bulkhead and this with transverse ones provided for eight sets of tanks. These were separated from the coal bunkers and machinery space by the pump-room, which also acted as a cofferdam. A fore and aft continuous trunkway was provided to allow for expansion,

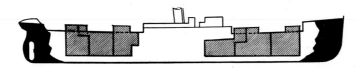

1886. The s.s. *Chigwell*, a dry cargo ship, which in 1886 was converted to carry oil in bulk. She measured 250 ft. in length by 34.5 ft. beam, and had a d.w. capacity of 2,150 tons. A very successful ship, she lasted well into this century, finishing up as an oil barge in Far Eastern waters.

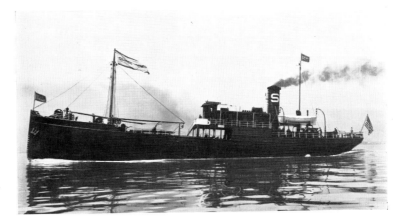

The s.s. *George Loomis* of 1896. Here this pioneer Pacific tanker is shown in her final rig, as owned by the Standard Oil Co., San Francisco. She had a gross tonnage of 691, and was fitted with a single-screw reciprocating engine of 460 s.h.p. which gave her a speed of 9 knots. She was finally lost in a gale in 1918.

The s.s. *Caucase*, built for Belgium by Armstrong Mitchell & Co. Ltd. in 1888, was one of the most successful of the early tankers. A ship of 1,675 tons gross and 2,750 tons d.w. (final figures), she measured 250.0 ft. × 35.2 ft. × 24.4 ft. depth of hold. Her machinery — of triple-expansion type—was made by the Wallsend Slipway Co. Ltd. Subsequently renamed *Ioannis Coutzis* and *Lille*, she was bought in the early 'twenties by the Norwegian whaling firm of Bryde & Dahl. Shown here as their *Thor Minor*, she bore this name until 1933. She was then sold to H. A. Dreesen, of Rotterdam, given Panamanian registry and renamed *Wilhelmine*. As such she operated for about a year on the North Atlantic before being scrapped at the age of forty-six.

The prototype of the tanker today—the famous *Gluckauf*, of 1886. A ship of 2,307 tons gross, she was built by Armstrong Whitworth for the German-American Petroleum Co. with dimensions 300.5 ft. × 37.2 ft. × 23.2 ft. She had a triple-expansion engine taking steam from two boilers at 150 lb. pressure. She operated successfully until 1893, when she stranded on Fire Island, near New York, her wreck being sold for £2,150. She was followed later in 1886 by a sister, named *Vorwarts*, built for another German firm, C. Wedekind & Co. This vessel was lost at sea in July, 1890.

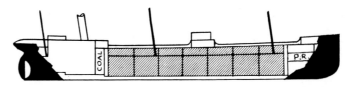

Section through the s.s. *Henri Reith*, one of the most successful tankers of 1892. She had seven pairs of tanks, with the pump-room right forward. Reserve bunkers were carried to port and starboard, either side of the central feed trunk. Built by R. Craggs & Sons Ltd., of Middlesbrough, for the Lennard Carrying Co. Ltd., she measured 280 ft. × 38.5 ft. × 18 ft. and had a gross tonnage of 2,265.

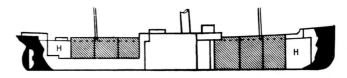

The s.s. *Mexicano*, built 1893 by Laing, Sunderland, for the King Steamship Line, Middlesbrough. An engines-amidships vessel measuring 270.0 ft. × 38.2 ft. × 22.6 ft., she was designed to carry oil one way and general cargo or molasses the other. As shown in the section through the fore hold, she had a centreline bulkhead only. At the extreme ends of the ship there were two dry cargo holds. When in hot climates awnings were rigged fore and aft, to prevent the overheating of her cargo.

The s.s. *City of Everett*, a whaleback tanker of 2,504 tons gross, which was built for the Standard Oil Co. in 1894 by the American Steel Barge Co., Everett, Wis. She had a length of 361.0 ft., a breadth of 42.0 ft. and a depth of 26.6 ft. The machinery was of triple expansion type. One of the first steamers in the Port Arthur Oil trade, she was gutted by fire at Beaumont in 1903, but was later rebuilt as shown here.

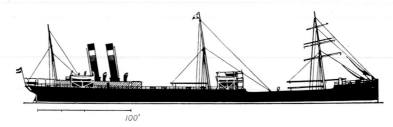

The *Rotterdam*, one of the very few two-funnelled tankers, was built for the American Petroleum Co., Rotterdam, by Palmers' Co. Ltd., Newcastle. A ship of 4,114 tons gross and about 5,900 tons d.w., she measured 366.3 ft. × 47.5 ft. × 25 ft. draught. A triple expansion engine of 2,200 i.h.p. and four Scotch boilers gave her a speed of about 10½ knots. Sold to Italy in the early nineteen-twenties and renamed *Olandese*, she was finally scrapped about ten years later.

lighter oils being carried each side of this. Triple expansion engines were fitted and these gave her a steady 10 knots. The steam pressure was 150 lb. The greatest attention was given to strength and the hull—part steel and part iron—was boiler riveted throughout, to prevent any chance of leakage. The vessel was equipped with powerful pumps and was electrically lighted. The *Gluckauf*, which was launched in 1885 and delivered her first cargo at Geestemunde in July, 1886, was followed almost immediately by a sister ship, the less well-known *Vorwarts* (2,466 tons gross), which was lost at sea in July, 1890.

The *Gluckauf*, although constructed in Britain, was not British owned, and it was the *Bakuin* that became famous as the first British built and owned tanker. Constructed by Wm. Gray & Co., West Hartlepool, in 1886, to the order of Mr. Alfred Suart, she measured 260.4 ft. in length, 36.0 ft. in breadth and had a gross tonnage of 1,669. Her internal design seems strange by present-day standards. She had a cellular bottom, the crown of which formed the base of the tanks. From here to the level of the 'tween decks the oil extended to the sides. On that deck, however, there were extra

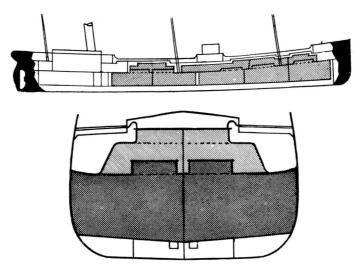

Sections through s.s. *Bakuin* of 1886. The first tank steamer to be built and owned in Britain, she was launched a week after the *Gluckauf*. Built for Mr. A. Suart of London by Wm. Gray & Co., she had a gross tonnage of 1,669 and measured 260.4 ft. × 36.0 ft. × 17.5 ft. The cross section shows how the upper tanks stopped short of the deck as a precaution against overheating when in the tropics. The *Bakuin*, which had a cargo capacity of 1,950 tons, could discharge in twelve hours. She was lost by fire off Peru in September, 1902. (in lower drawing expansion tanks are shown with lighter tint.)

The *Saxoleine* of 1899, owned by the Saxoleine S.S. Co. Ltd., was the sixth tanker to be built for the Hunting group. A ship of 3,757 tons gross and 5,700 tons d.w. (length 336 ft., breadth 45 ft.), she was constructed by Armstrong Whitworth & Co. In 1928 she was sold to become the Italian *Celeno*. Later, in 1943, she was taken over by Germany and renamed *Claudia*. Two years afterwards she was seized by the U.S.S.R. when in the Black Sea. She was a sister to the Lane & MacAndrews tankers *Luciline* and *Oriflamme*.

oil compartments which did not reach either to the deck above or to the hull sides. It was thought that the main tanks, being immersed, would not incur any appreciable rise of temperature in hot climates, while the upper ones would not reach such a high temperature as they would if they extended the full width and height. The ship was given an extra bulkhead amidships to permit the carriage of several grades of oil without fear of contamination. Valves controlling the discharge of cargo were placed aft, in the engine room. Electric lighting was installed, while to minimise the danger of fire 'her cabins were heated by steam instead of by coal fires.' Despite these precautions it was by fire that she was eventually lost, while in a floating dock at Callao in September, 1902. So bad was her state afterwards that the local Lloyd's surveyor advised her owners that the wreck when sold would not fetch more than £50.

The successful operation of pioneers like the *Gluckauf* and *Bakuin* showed that most of the major technical problems had been overcome, and as a result the closing years of the 'eighties brought a rush, both for the building of new tankers and also for the conversion of many existing dry cargo steamers. The firm of Sir W. G. Armstrong Mitchell & Co. Ltd. (later Sir W. G. Armstrong & Co. Ltd., then Sir W. G. Armstrong Whitworth & Co. Ltd., whose shipyard now forms part of Vickers-Armstrongs Ltd.) continued building along the lines of the *Gluckauf*, and during ensuing years stood out as the giant among British tanker builders.

But they were not alone, and other north-east coast firms such as Wm. Gray & Co. Ltd.: Sir James Laing & Sons: Swan, Hunter, & Wigham Richardson Ltd.: the Tyne Iron Shipbuilding Co. Ltd.: W. Dobson & Co.: R. Craggs & Sons and R. & W. Hawthorn Leslie & Co. Ltd. soon had a number of tank steamers to their credit. Of Clydeside firms, where interest developed rather later, the names perhaps most prominent were A. & J. Inglis Ltd.: D. J. Dunlop & Co. and Scotts' Shipbuilding & Engineering Co. Ltd. A Forthside yard which also featured among early tanker builders was the Grangemouth Dockyard Co. Ltd. Two notable Scandinavian pioneers were Burmeister & Wain, of Copenhagen, and the Lindholmen-Motala shipyard.

In the year 1886 the number of steamers carrying petroleum in bulk totalled only about a dozen, yet so great was the output during the next few years that by 1891 there were between eighty and ninety operating on the Atlantic alone. The first tank steamer to be built in America appeared in 1886. Built for the Standard Oil Company, she was appropriately named *Standard*.

With this great surge in tanker construction many new tanker-owning firms came into being, joined by others which had hitherto been only interested in shipbroking or tramp ship owning. Amongst early British firms which stand out in this respect are Lane & MacAndrew, H. E. Moss & Co., the Prince Line, Alfred Suart, the Bear Creek Oil & Shipping Co. Ltd., the Burmah Oil Co., John M. Lennard & Sons Ltd., the Northern Petroleum Tank S.S. Co. Ltd. and Hunting & Son Ltd.

One of the early oil distributing concerns in the United Kingdom was the Kerosene Co., which was formed in 1887 by Lane & MacAndrew. Out of it grew the Anglo Caucasian Oil Co., a firm which later became the Consolidated and finally, after an amalgamation, the British Petroleum Co. (not to be confused with the present firm of this name). Amongst other similar new ventures the most important was the Homelight Oil Co., which distributed Russian oil in this country.

The firm of H. E. Moss & Co. became connected with the oil carrying trade in 1886, when the importation of bulk petroleum was only beginning. This well-known concern was started by Mr. H. E. Moss in 1840, the

London office being opened in 1862 and the Newcastle one in 1889. Liverpool at that time had very poor and inadequate oil storage facilities. One of the first cargoes of bulk petroleum to be landed there came in the *Lux* in 1887, a 2,000-ton steamer owned by her builders, Armstrong Mitchell & Co. Soon afterwards—in 1889—Messrs. Moss, who had arranged the business handling of this, started building a fleet of their own: but at the same time they continued to charter tonnage and retain their interest in the shipbroking industry. Today several of their tankers perpetuate the names of the old pioneer vessels of the 'eighties.

As regards Continental tanker firms there were the German-American Petroleum Co., of Hamburg: the Societe Anonyme d'Armament, d'Industrie et de Commerce, of Antwerp, etc., while further east there were various Russian concerns. Of American firms the Standard Oil Co. was already of considerable size and this, in the late 'eighties, decided to enter the European market. It did so by a process of purchase and amalgamation: the result being the largest tanker deal to date, involving sixteen ships, amongst them the famous *Gluckauf*. They also formed the Anglo-American Oil Co. Ltd., which in a matter of a few years attained the premier position in the North Atlantic oil trade.

3

Anglo-American and Shell

THE year 1888 was one of great activity for those concerned with the tanker industry, and in it Armstrong Mitchell & Co. built no fewer than twelve tankers. Coinciding with a new era as regards the importation of American oil into Britain and the Continent, there came the formation of the Anglo-American Oil Co. Ltd. This concern started by buying about a dozen second-hand vessels, some specially designed as tankers, others converted, but the following year saw the building by A. & J. Inglis of their first new vessel, the 3,294-ton *Bayonne* which, rather surprisingly, was launched sideways. She measured 330.0 ft. by 42.2 ft., had a carrying capacity of 4,000 tons and was used for carrying petroleum from the U.S.A. to the company's main depot which was at London (Purfleet), and others at Hull, Liverpool and Bristol. The *Bayonne* had nine pairs of tanks, with a cargo pump at each end, and together these were capable of discharging her cargo in ten hours. In appearance she was not dissimilar to the *Bakuin*, having three islands, a single funnel aft and three masts, although the mizzen was stepped much closer to the funnel.

Other additions that year were the similar but Dunlop-built *Manhattan* (3,284 tons) and the *Kasbek* and *Darial*, ships of 2,707 and 2,767 tons gross which had been built a year previously by Armstrong Mitchell for London owners. These were renamed *Suwanee* and *Genesee* respectively. These, however, were quite outclassed by a trio built on the Clyde, 1893-94, the *Delaware* and *Lackawanna*, both from Dunlops and of 3,855 tons, and the 3,868-ton *Potomac*, which came from A. & J. Inglis. The Company had very definite views as to their requirements and at the time of their completion these three were regarded as the last word in tanker design. The *Potomac*

C

The s.s. *Potomac* of 1893. One of the crack tankers of her day, she was built for the Anglo-American Oil Co. by A. & J. Inglis, of Glasgow. 3,858 tons gross, 5,490 tons d.w. Length 345.2 ft., breadth 44.2 ft. She was wrecked off the Bahamas in 1929.

is reputed to have had a service speed of over 13 knots, but this may have been an exaggeration. However, in ten years she made over two hundred crossings of the Atlantic. So soundly were they built that the *Potomac* and *Delaware* continued in service until the late 'twenties, when the former was wrecked and the other scrapped at Blyth. The *Lackawanna* lasted many years longer: exchanged for a larger ship from the German-American Petroleum Co. in 1910, she bore various names and flags before being torpedoed in 1941 as the Italian *Maya*.

Even at this time it was not unusual for tankers to take oil one way and dry cargo the other. The Anglo-American's *Seminole* provided an example of this on her maiden voyage. Built by Furness Withy in 1904, she had a length of 414 ft. and was fitted with 14 transverse bulkheads besides a centreline one which extended through both the oil tanks and expansion trunks. On her first voyage from the Tyne on July 27th, she proceeded to Novorossisk, where she loaded bulk oil—nearly 7,000 tons—for Calcutta. She there loaded jute for Dundee, where she discharged in November, after a round trip of under four months.

Shipbuilders and naval architects were now faced with another major design problem, the result of the growing increase in length of tankers. Many advocated the placing of machinery amidships. By so doing, they argued, there would be less strain when a vessel was in ballast or experiencing heavy weather, and that she could be trimmed more easily. For some years this argument held sway and it seemed as if only the smaller tankers would have their engines aft. However, the extra cost and waste of space which resulted from a long shaft tunnel caused designers to redouble their efforts in finding a solution, and in this they were eventually successful.

With these factors in mind the Anglo-American chose an amidships machinery position for their *Tuscarora,* which they had built in 1898 by Laing, of Sunderland. With a gross tonnage of 6,117 and a length of 420 ft., she was by far the largest tanker in the world. She proved so successful that the Company used her as the prototype for the yet larger *Narraganset,* a ship of 9,196 tons gross and 12,500 tons deadweight, which was built in 1903 by Scott's Shipbuilding & Engineering Co. Ltd. This truly remarkable vessel, which was ahead of her time, was the first tanker to be built at this yard. Like many others in the company's fleet, she was named after an American river, a fact which resulted in the firm often being referred to as the 'River Line.'

The *Narraganset* measured 512 ft. in length b.p. (531 ft. overall) by 63 ft. 3 in. breadth moulded by 42 ft. depth moulded, and had a load displacement of 21,000 tons on a draught of 27 ft. She had three decks, 18 transverse bulkheads and her oil compartments were subdivided by

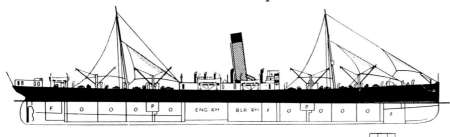

Above: The *Narraganset,* 9,196 tons gross, was built by Scotts in 1903 for the Anglo-American Oil Co. Ltd. Then the world's largest tanker, she had a d.w. tonnage of 12,500 and an overall length of 531 ft. She was torpedoed off the Scillies in March, 1917. (F denotes fuel tanks, O oil compartments and P pump rooms.)

Right: A cross section through the *Narraganset* showing the position of the pump-room. The space beyond this on the lower of the 'tween decks served as an expansion trunk.

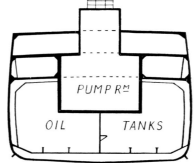

two longitudinal bulkheads to form 27 separate tanks. The shaft tunnel was circular and ran through eight oil compartments. Steam connections were fitted for cleaning tanks and for fire extinguishing, while a large fan fitted in each pumproom connected to each tank for the supply and suction of air. Besides these there were many cowls on deck which were connected to the tanks by portable pipes. Built at a time when many tankers were laid up, she was so designed that she could carry general cargo at the sides of the 'tween decks, which could alternatively be used to carry troops or cattle. She was fitted with nine steam winches and sixteen derricks, also a full spread of canvas to protect her cargo in very hot weather. Her machinery consisted of a massive triple expansion engine of 5,500 i.h.p. This took steam at 200 p.s.i. from six boilers and gave a speed of over 13 knots. A study of her performance shows that on one of her best trips she did the round Atlantic voyage in 27 days, this being from Tyne to New York in ballast and back to the Thames with a full cargo of 12,000 tons. Her career ended in March, 1917, when she was lost off the Scilly Islands together with all her crew, after being torpedoed.

A ship destined to become even more famous was the 9,202-ton *Iroquois*, launched by Harland & Wolff, Belfast, on June 27th, 1907. Not only was she the first large tank steamer to be fitted with twin screws, but she was designed to tow a barge of almost equal size regularly to and fro across the Atlantic. Compared with the *Narraganset*, the *Iroquois* was shorter and relatively more beamy, measuring 476 ft. in length b.p. by 60 ft. breadth moulded by 35 ft. 5 in. depth moulded. She was fitted with two sets of quadruple expansion engines which took steam from four boilers and gave her a speed of over 10 knots laden, even with her tow. A very strongly built vessel, she had a long and successful career, not being broken up until 1947.

The tankers of fifty years ago were less uniform in appearance than those of today and this particularly applied to the units of the Anglo-American fleet. The *Cheyenne*, built by Swan Hunter in 1908, was a smaller ship with a gross tonnage of 4,987 and a length of 388 ft., yet she sported two funnels, stepped very close together and each of them serving two boilers. The result was a very distinctive profile shared only by two others of similar size

The s.s. *Osceola*, 393 tons gross, one of Britain's pioneer coastal tankers. Built in 1897 for the Anglo-American Oil Co. Ltd. by D. J. Dunlop & Co., Port Glasgow, she was designed to distribute oil to the Company's depots in Ireland and the South of England and continued in this trade until the 'thirties. She carried 380 tons on a draught of 10 ft. Length 140.5 ft., breadth 26.1 ft. Triple-expansion machinery, speed 9 knots.

The s.s. *Ashtabula*, 7,025 tons gross. Built and engined 1903 by Palmers Co. Ltd., Newcastle, as the *Graf Stroganoff* for the Northern S.S. Co. St. Petersburg, and bought later by the Anglo-American Oil Co. Ltd., she remained in their fleet until 1930, when she was sold to become the Italian *Alabama*, 8,975 tons d.w. Length 428 ft., breadth 54.7 ft. Triple-expansion engines, speed 10½ knots. Sister ships, also built by Palmers, were the *New York* of 1902 and the *Prometheus* of 1903.

The t.s.s. *Iroquois*, 9,202 tons gross. One of the most notable tankers of her day, she was built for the Anglo-American Oil Co. in 1907 by Harland & Wolff, Belfast, and was the first large tanker to be given twin screws. Of 11,800 tons d.w., she measured 476.3 ft. in length and had a beam of 60.3 ft. She had quad.-expansion machinery and four boilers which gave her a speed of 10 knots, even when towing the barge *Navahoe*. She was scrapped in 1947.

and date, the Admiralty owned *Delphinula* and H. E. Moss & Co.'s *Lucigen*, together with the older and rather smaller *Rotterdam*.

By this time the Anglo-American Oil Company had grown almost beyond recognition. Primarily interested in the marketing of illuminating oil, it controlled the greatest oil distributing organisation in the United Kingdom. It also owned the largest fleet of oil carrying vessels under the Red Ensign. This in 1907 comprised nineteen ocean-going tank steamers, four case-oil steamers and sixteen sailing ships: amongst which was the *Narraganset*, the world's largest tanker.

The year 1892 saw the beginnings of another world-famous tanker fleet—that of Shell. Its founder, Marcus Samuel (later Sir Marcus and then Lord Bearsted) was the second son of a London merchant, whose original business in Oriental curios, shell covered boxes, etc., had grown enormously. Marcus Samuel first became interested in oil after making a visit to Japan in search of curios. He then investigated the possibilities of shipping Russian case oil to the Far East and building up a connection such as the Standard Oil Company had done in China. The result was that a year later he entered into a contract with a Rothschild controlled Russian group of producers and refiners—known as BNITO—for the supply of kerosene at Batum. He at once started to ship and sell it in cased form in the Eastern market with which he was so familiar.

His first ship was the *Murex*, which was launched by William Gray in May, 1892. While she was building, and despite great opposition from other firms, Samuel won a concession from the Suez Canal Company which permitted him to send tankers through the canal—a privilege not granted to other tanker owners until six years later. In the course of 1892 the *Murex* was completed and made tanker history in being the first of her type to make transit through that waterway.

In the early days the fleet consisted of five ships, of two separate classes; the pioneer *Murex* and her sisters *Conch* and *Clam*, each of just over 3,550 tons gross and 4,500 tons deadweight and fitted with pumps capable of discharging their cargo in twelve hours. The others were the rather larger pair *Turbo* and *Elax* of 5,500 tons deadweight, but of otherwise similar design. Considering the origins of the family business and the fact that he was an authority on shells, it was natural that he should name his vessels after various species of these. A specimen of the appropriate shell was also carried in each ship, and as some of these were extremely rare and valuable, they proved a source of embarrassment to the captains, having to be locked up when in port.

The firm of M. Samuel & Co. continued to operate until October, 1897, when its fleet numbered fourteen ships. In that year the Shell Transport & Trading Co. Ltd. was formed, with a capital of £1,800,000 in £100 shares. This coincided with a Russian decision to transport oil to Vladivostock, using only ships under their own flag. Fearing the possibility of an attempted Russian monopoly on a wider scale, Samuel set about widening his interests. He acquired concessions in Borneo and so became interested in oil producing. A refinery was built at Balik Papan, and this with the laying of pipe lines and the purchase of coastal craft and other equipment necessitated the raising of further capital. A chain of oil depots had by now been established in the Far East, despite bitter opposition from the Standard Oil and Royal Dutch concerns. Later Samuel entered into further agreements with American and other interests and so became assured of world-wide supplies. In 1907, when the Shell Company had a fleet of 25 ships and the Royal Dutch owned nine, the two companies amalgamated. Two new operating companies were formed, the Anglo-Saxon Petroleum Co. Ltd., which took over the Shell fleet and its Dutch counterpart Bataafsche Petroleum Maatschappij, the two firms being responsible for the management of affairs in their respective countries.

Turning to the ships themselves, it was customary for a number of years for these to carry oil outwards and return with general cargo, and this had its effect on the external appearance in the shape of extra kingposts and derricks. There was a steady flow of new vessels to join the original five-unit fleet. Amongst this second series were the Gray-built *Volute* of 1893 and the rather later *Nerite*.

In 1894 one of Suart's tankers, the 3,708-ton *Baku Standard*, attracted great attention in being the first oil-fired steamer to cross the Atlantic. A few years later, in 1898, two small vessels which were building for Shell were fitted to burn either coal or oil. These were the Armstrong-built

Trigonia and *Haliotis,* both of some 1,600 tons and designed for service in the East. In contrast to the earlier ship which was given Wallsend type burners, these two were fitted with Fortescue Flannery type. A year later, following their success, the Shell Company converted their six-year-old *Clam* to burn oil fuel exclusively. Previously as a coal burner she had consumed about 26 tons per day under three boilers, this for an average speed of 9 knots. This was cut down to 18 tons of oil under two boilers, for an average of 9 knots, the stokehold crew at the same time being reduced to four. The results achieved in this ship and in the *Volute,* which was similarly altered in 1900, paved the way for the gradual conversion of the whole Shell fleet.

In 1889, when Borneo was attracting attention as a liquid fuel producing centre, the Shell Company went in for much larger vessels of the *Cardium* and *Bulysses* classes, which ranked amongst the world's largest tankers. The *Bulysses* was launched in May, 1900, and was the third of her class to be built for the firm by Armstrong Whitworth. She had a total deadweight capacity of 8,500 tons and displaced 13,270 tons, her main dimensions being length overall 426 ft., breadth 52 ft. and depth moulded 34 ft. Built to the highest class of Lloyd's Register and to conform to Suez Canal regulations, her design was that of a dual cargo ship, capable of carrying petroleum in bulk or general cargo. Her propelling machinery consisted of a triple expansion engine of 2,200 i.h.p. which took steam at 180 lb. pressure from three large single-ended boilers, each of which had four furnaces fitted to burn oil or coal. The ship had a speed of 9 knots and was fitted throughout with electric light. The cargo pumps were capable of discharging her cargo in twelve hours.

Progress was so great that by 1902 the firm had built or bought 38 steamers of 152,000 tons deadweight and stood fourth in order of all British lines using the Suez Canal. One of the ships built that year was the *Pectan,* which was even larger than the *Bulysses* and came before the public eye by towing off a battleship, H.M.S. *Victorious,* which had gone ashore near Suez. Shell tankers were kept at a remarkably high level of efficiency, but then, as now, the occasional accident did occur, and the reason for the loss of one of their earlier ships was rather remarkable. Caught in a sand-

The s.s. *Volute* of 1893, one of the earliest units of the Shell Transport & Trading Co.'s fleet. She had a gross tonnage of 4,006 and measured 347 ft. × 45.6 ft. × 26.7 ft. She was one of a trio built that year for Shell by Wm. Gray & Co., the others being the *Bullmouth* and *Elax*. The fitting of the donkey boiler funnel outside the main one was then common practice.

The s.s. *Nerite*, 6,200 tons d.w., one of the twenty-four vessels in the original Shell fleet, seen discharging the first cargo of liquid fuel at Suez in October, 1899. A few years later, in March, 1902, she was burnt out on the Great Bitter Lakes while taking cargo off the stranded tanker *Bulysses*. Note the auxiliary funnel aft of the main one, the many kingposts and the unusually long bridge deck with cargo hatch at its after end.

The s.s. *Havre*, a case oil carrier of 2,073 tons gross built for the Shell fleet in 1905 by Wm. Gray & Co. Ltd., West Hartlepool. She was of 3,190 tons d.w. and measured 288 ft. in length and 39.0 ft. in breadth. Triple-expansion machinery gave a speed of 9 knots. She was torpedoed in June, 1942, between Alexandria and Matruh.

storm in March, 1902, the *Bulysses* ran aground in the Great Bitter Lake. A local tank steamer owned by the Suez Canal Company was at once sent to help lighten her. She was joined later by the Shell tanker *Nerite* which, it was planned, would take off the rest of the larger ship's cargo in two loads, discharging it at Suez. However, in their zeal to assist, those on the *Nerite* took on board too much, resulting in her cargo space being completely filled. Expansion of the cargo burst the after cofferdam and let the oil flow freely into the stokehold. The ship was set on fire and acted as a lamp until the whole of the oil cargo was burnt out.

One of the longest lived of these ships was the 6,163-ton *Strombus*, a contemporary of the *Bulysses*. After many years service as an oil tanker she was adapted to meet the needs of the whaling industry and continued in operation until the second world war, when she was sunk.

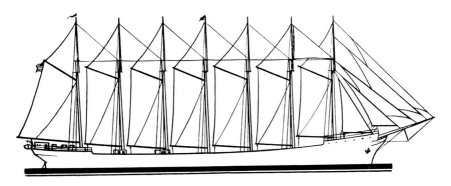

The *Thomas W. Lawson*, 5,218 tons gross. The world's only seven-masted schooner, she was built by the Fore River S.B. Co., Quincy, Mass., in 1902. After early use on the U.S. coast carrying coal, she was converted into a bulk oil carrier. She was wrecked on the Scilly Islands in December, 1907.

4

Oil Sailers and Barges

THE rapid development of the oil industry provided a much needed form of employment for the sailing ship from the 'eighties to the early part of the present century: this at a time when sail was being steadily displaced from other trades by steam. Their slow speed was no disadvantage and one tank sailer, the 1,694-ton *Calcutta*, continued on the trans-Atlantic service until 1921. While the number of bulk oil sailing ships in service at any one time was never very great, the total number built was somewhere in the region of 250. A great many others were also used to carry cased oil, some regularly, others just occasionally.

Outstanding among American sailing tankers was the *Thomas W. Lawson*, a great schooner—the only one ever to boast seven masts—which was built by the Fore River Shipbuilding Co., at Quincy, Mass., in 1902. She measured 385 ft. in length overall by 50 ft. breadth by 35.2 ft. in depth to upper deck. Unlike most schooners, she was built of steel throughout, even to the lower masts. Topmasts and other spars alone were of wood. Sails and steering were handled by steam and despite her great size— 5,218 tons gross—she only needed a crew of sixteen men. Originally designed to carry coal in the U.S. coastal trade, she was converted about a year later by the Newport News shipyard to carry oil in bulk, following which she spent several years on the U.S. coast, taking Texas oil to Philadelphia. The *Thomas W. Lawson* was next used by the Anglo-American Oil Co. to bring a cargo of oil to Europe, but in December, 1907, just as she was nearing the end of this, her first trans-Atlantic voyage, she came to grief on the Scillies. Sheltering there during a hurricane, she broke adrift and became a total wreck.

By far the most important fleet of oil sailers was that owned by the Anglo-American Oil Co., which in period 1904-07 numbered as many as sixteen. These ranged in size from the *Calcutta*, 1,694 tons gross, to the *Brilliant*, which measured 3,765 gross. Between these limits came the *Alcides, Arras, Comet, Daylight, Drumeltan, Eclipse, Glendoon, Johanne, Juteopolis, Kentmere, King George, Lawhill, Lyndhurst* and *Radiant*. Many of these, however, were case-oil carriers and like the *Lawhill, Juteopolis* and *Drumeltan*, etc., had been bought second-hand. The *Lawhill*, for example, was a four-masted barque built in 1892 and of 2,942 tons. She was originally employed in the jute trade until her purchase by the Anglo-American in 1899. She then operated in the case-oil trade until 1911, when she was sold to a Liverpool firm. Eight years were to elapse before she passed into the Erikson fleet to start the best known phase of her career.

The *Lawhill's* movements for 1906 reveal that she left Cape Town on July 3rd and arrived at New York on August 20th, a mean effective speed in the desired direction of just under 6 knots. She was then in New York for 34 days discharging, undergoing repairs in dry dock and reloading before leaving New York on September 23rd for Cape Town, where she arrived 70 days later. Another Anglo-American sailing ship made the passage from Cape Town to New York in 39 days in 1907. This was the *Glendoon* of 1,981 tons, built in 1894. The *Drumeltan*, an iron four-masted barque of about 2,000 tons gross was built in 1883. A few years later she

The *Brilliant*, built for the Anglo-American Oil Co. Ltd. in 1901 by Russell & Co., Port Glasgow. She had a steel hull, measured 352.5 ft. × 49.1 ft. and was originally used as a case oil carrier, although she and her sister *Daylight* were later converted to carry oil in bulk. Each had a single oil-cargo pump of 100 tons capacity. She is shown leaving her builders' yard after completion.

was in the case-oil trade and remained in it until 1905. The movements records reveal that in that year the *Drumeltan* left New York on February 24th and arrived at Brisbane early in June, after a run of 104 days.

Another sailing ship owned by the same concern was the *King George*, which operated between Bayonne (New Jersey) and Hong Kong, Shanghai and other Chinese ports. Captain William Tucker, who served on the *King George* from 1904 onwards, has recently described one of these voyages in these terms; 'We carried about 120,000 cases (there were two five-gallon cans of oil per case) outward bound to the East and returned with Chinese matting, fireworks and "notions." A round trip took nine or ten months.' The *King George* was eventually wrecked south of Sumatra in 1909.

Between 1900 and 1903 the Anglo-American had eight large sailing ships specially built in the United Kingdom for the oil trade. Two of these

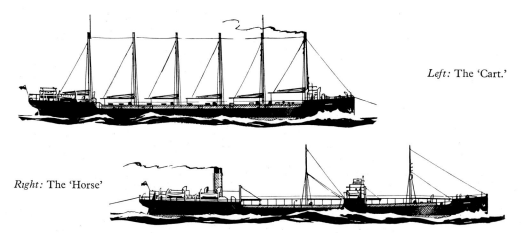

Left: The 'Cart.'

Right: The 'Horse'

The tanker *Iroquois* and barge *Navahoe*, which were familiarly known as 'The Cart and Horse.' Built in 1907 and 1908 for the Anglo-American, they plied across the Atlantic for many years with great success. In heavy weather, when the strain became too great, the tow was sometimes slipped. According to one story often told at sea, the *Navahoe* on one such occasion, under sail alone, reached her destination ahead of the *Iroquois*. Between them they had a d.w. capacity of over 18,000 tons.

were the *Brilliant* and *Eclipse*. The former, a steel four-masted barque of 3,765 tons gross, was built by Russell's, of Port Glasgow, in 1901, and cost about £54,000. With her sister ship, the *Daylight*, she was the largest four-masted sailing ship in the world, having a length of about 350 ft. and a breadth of 49 ft. The specification for the building of the *Brilliant*, dated 1900, provided that the captain's room was to be 'comfortably fitted up with berth (i.e. sleeping bunk), drawers, sofa with seat and back stuffed and covered with Utrecht velvet, table and chronometer stand, book-shelves and washstand with enamelled top."

The mate had a room of his own, but the second and third mates shared one. All the rest of the crew were housed in a deckhouse, a space required by the specification to be fitted with berths for crew, with teak skylight, and to have lockers and seats, the ventilation to approval of Board of Trade surveyors. Those who have inspected the very spacious and well-equipped officers' and crews' quarters of a large modern tanker will appreciate what a tremendous advance has taken place in the amenities provided.

The movements record for 1904-05 shows the *Brilliant* leaving New York on July 31st with oil in cases and arriving at Yokohama on January 8th, a passage of 161 days. In 1910 she was fitted at New York for the carriage of oil in bulk and continued to trade for the same owners until 1913. By way of comparison the *Eclipse,* built by Rodgers in 1902, made the voyage from New York to Hong Kong during 1905 in only 107 days.

The Anglo-American sailer fleet was disposed of about 1911, although one unit, the *Calcutta* (1,694 tons gross, built 1892) was retained much longer. During the latter part of the 1914-18 war this vessel, which had five tanks, was used to carry oil fuel for destroyers. After the war she was returned to her owners to make a few more trans-Atlantic crossings. She left New York with her last cargo for the U.K. on July 21st, 1921, arriving at Avonmouth on August 14th. After that she was withdrawn, used for a short spell as a fuel barge and then scrapped.

The Standard Oil Co., which adopted the idea of bulk oil carrying about 1892, developed their fleet along very different lines. Besides owning some fine oil sailers and tank steamers they built up a fleet of large tank barges. These were primarily intended for use along the U.S. Atlantic and Pacific seaboards, but some of the larger ones were even towed round the Horn, from New York to San Francisco, to Japan and across the Atlantic. Amongst the tankers used for these early long distance tows were the *Atlas, Captain A. F. Lucas* and *Colonel E. L. Drake.* At this time the company owned about a dozen such barges, as well as many small ones. Largest of all in this category was the 360-ft. long *S.O.Co. No.* 94, a four-master of 4,167 tons gross, which had been designed and built as such in 1903. Many of the Standard Oil Co.'s smaller barges, however, were conversions, or formerly power-driven ships. An example of this can be found in their pioneer tank steamer *Standard,* which had been built at Chester, Pa., in 1888, with dimensions 162.1 ft. by 30.1 ft., Lloyd's Register of 1904/05 shows her still in her original owner's service, but as the 589-ton barge *S.O.Co. of N.Y. No.* 56.

The success of these large barges led to the building of a most notable pair of ships, the *Iroquois* and *Navahoe,* which were constructed at Belfast in 1907-08 for the Anglo-American Oil Co. These owners seem to have been reluctant to see the approaching end of the sailing ships and hit on a compromise which was remarkably successful.

The *Iroquois* carried about 8,800 tons of cargo (usually refined oil from

U.S. Gulf ports to Purfleet) and towed the *Navahoe*, which carried about 9,250 tons (usually spirit from Gulf ports to Thameshaven). The *Navahoe's* lines were certainly not those of a sailing ship, but she was rigged as a six-masted schooner. A steam winch was provided at each mast for hoisting the sails, which were always set as long as they would draw, but with a fair wind they were sometimes blown out of the bolt ropes before they could be taken in. The foremast of the *Navahoe* also acted as the funnel for the boiler which supplied steam to the towing winch, cargo pumps and auxiliaries. The skippers of these ships were usually on good terms, but used to 'take the mike out of one another' by referring to 'my barge skipper' or 'my tugboat skipper,' as the case might be.

Between March, 1908, and May, 1917, the *Iroquois* and *Navahoe* made 148 Atlantic crossings, usually U.S.A. Gulf to London with refined oil and spirit, at an average speed of 8.7 knots. In May, 1917, the convoy system being in operation on the Atlantic crossing, the two ships were transferred to the U.S.A. Gulf to Halifax run, carrying fuel oil for the Admiralty at an average speed of 10.1 knots. In November, 1918, they returned to their original Gulf-London run, remaining until 1930, when the *Navahoe* became a storage hulk in the Caribbean area.

The *Iroquois* continued to run solo from 1930, but occasionally took special assignments in her stride, including the towing out of the submarine pipelines at Tripoli and Haifa Bay in 1934, and at Mena Al Ahmadi in 1946. During the second world war her feats included the towage of a U.S. Navy dry dock from Honolulu to the South Sea Islands and of the tanker *San Gaspar* (a war casualty) from Trinidad to Key West. The *Navahoe* ended her days when she was ceremoniously 'buried at sea' in 1936 off Trinidad: the *Iroquois* was sold to U.K. shipbreakers in 1947.

Amongst other notable oil-sailers was the *Andromeda*, regarded by Germans as 'the first overseas tank ship of the world.' She was built in England but bought by the German-American Petroleum Co., who in 1885 converted her into a tank ship at the Tecklenborg yard at Geestemunde. The conversion increased her capacity from 12,000 to 17,000 barrels. In 1888 the *Andromeda* stranded near Yarmouth, having made five trips and transported about 70,000 barrels of kerosene from the U.S.A. to Europe.

The m.s. *Deodata* of 1897. Built as the four-masted French sailing tanker *Quevilly*, she was later fitted with small auxiliary motors. Sold to Chr. Hannevig, of Aasgaardstrand, Norway, in the early 'twenties, she was then converted into a full powered motor ship. Gross tonnage as built 3,482, finally 3,295. Dimensions 324.8 ft. × 45.5 ft. Sunk October, 1939. The light, black topped funnel by the main mast is that of a tug alongside.

The steel six-masted tank barge *Navahoe*, which was built for the Anglo-American Oil Co. in 1908 by Harland & Wolff, Belfast. Her long partnership with the tanker *Iroquois* finished about 1930, when she became a storage hulk off the mouth of the River Carapito, Venezuela, topping up the large ships after they had crossed the local bar. She was eventually towed to sea and scuttled. Gross tonnage 7,718. Length b.p. 450.2 ft., breadth 48.3 ft.

The *Myrshell*, 2,636 tons gross, after her conversion into a tanker. Built by McMillan in 1902 as the four-masted barque *Ama Begonakoa*, she was owned until 1910 by the well-known Spanish firm of Sota y Aznar, after which she became famous as the *Medway*, a cadet training ship owned by Devitt & Moore. In 1919 she was fitted with two 4-stroke S.A. Vickers diesels which gave a speed of 9 knots. The *Myrshell*, which had a d.w. tonnage of 3,900, measured 300 ft. in length by 43.2 ft. beam She was broken up in Japan in 1933.

Windjammer to tanker—more Anglo-Saxon conversions.

The *Ortinashell*, 2,603 tons gross. Length 309 ft., breadth 42 ft. Built in 1891 as the four-masted barque *Oweenee* and first owned in Canada by Mr. F. C. Mahon, of Windsor, Nova Scotia. She was converted into a steam tanker by the Anglo-Saxon Petroleum Co. in 1917.

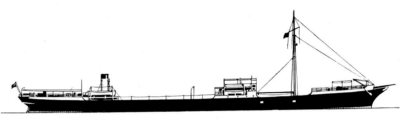

The *Scala Shell*, 3,585 tons gross. Length 330 ft., breadth 47 ft. Originally one of a large fleet of sailing ships owned by B. Wencke Sohne, of Hamburg, she was built by A. McMillan & Son in 1902. Her reconstruction from four-masted barque to tank steamer took place early in 1922.

Others were given a fresh lease of life by being fitted with the then new diesel engines. One of the earlier bulk oil carriers so converted was the *Quevilly*, a 3,482-ton four-masted barque built at Rouen in 1897 for the local firm of H. Prentout Le Blond & E. Leroux who, up to 1911, benefited under the French Subsidy Act. The ship, which as a sailer had proved very successful, was fitted with two diesels, albeit of rather modest power. These were replaced thirteen years later by new ones of greater output and the vessel continued in service until October, 1939, when she was sunk as the Norwegian-owned *Deodata*.

Another group deserves special mention; the various old sailers which, during the first world war, were converted into steam or motor tankers in order to alleviate the acute shortage of such tonnage. Amongst these were the *Dolbadarn Castle, Gladys, Medway, Oweenee, Speedonia*, etc., which started new careers under Anglo-Saxon ownership as the *Dolphin Shell, Gapern Shell, Myrshell, Ortinashell* and *Scala Shell* respectively.

The *Dolbadarn Castle*, 1,989 tons gross, was built by Hamilton in 1897, as the three-masted barque *Haytor* and subsequently became the *Earn-*

mount before being given her *Castle* name by Robert Thomas & Co., of Liverpool, a few years later. In 1918 she was taken in hand and fitted with two four-cylinder Bolinder oil engines which gave her a speed of 7 knots. These alterations naturally altered her tonnage somewhat, to 2,002 tons gross and 3,082 tons deadweight. She remained in the 'Shell' fleet until 1931, when she was sold for breaking up in Japan.

The *Gladys*, 1,363 tons, was of similar age and rig. A Bristol-built vessel, she was owned by Shaw Savill & Co. from 1897 to about 1912. After this she traded for the Tal Tal Shipping Co. until 1916, when she was resold, this time to the Anglo-Saxon Company. A couple of years later she had had her yards removed, masts cut down to stumps and was fitted with twin-screw diesels. But as a power-driven ship she had a short life, for she was wrecked on Mafameda Island in January, 1919.

The *Oweenee* was a larger four-masted barque of 2,432 tons gross, which had been built in 1891 by Richardson Duck & Co., of Stockton-on-Tees, for Canadian owners. One of the fastest of the later-day sailing ships, she measured 309 ft. by 42 ft. There were various changes of owner—until 1917 when she was bought by the Anglo-Saxon and converted into a single screw tank steamer. Under her final name—*Ortinashell*—she saw many years' service and well after the end of the last world war was still doing useful work in the Near East.

A later conversion with more sightly results was that of the 3,584-ton *Scala Shell*, which took place early in 1922. Built on the Clyde in 1902 as the 3,265-ton German-owned *Urania*, she also was originally a four-masted barque. Later she was renamed *Speedonia*, and it was as this that she was acquired by the Anglo-Saxon Petroleum Co. In her case twin-screw triple expansion machinery—by Cooper & Greig—was chosen and this gave her a speed of about 9 knots. In her final guise the *Scala Shell* carried about 4,900 tons deadweight on a draught of 24 ft. 9 in. She, too, eventually finished up in a shipbreaker's yard in Japan—in 1931, a year which saw the disposal of many of the Company's older ships.

5

Tankers 1900—1919

THE early part of the twentieth century was one of steady growth and consolidation as regards the size and design of tankers. The discovery of oil in Texas in 1900 within easy access of useful ports gave a great stimulus to new construction and resulted in a rapid increase in the number of new tankers built between that date and the outbreak of the first world war in 1914.

Many early vessels, however, suffered from structural weakness through being built too long for their depth, but the Isherwood longitudinal system of framing provided a new and far stronger form of construction admirably suited to tanker needs. The Foster King system of transverse framing, and the Miller system, which combined longitudinal and transverse, were two others which were adopted with much success. In 1909 the Shell Company in their Swan Hunter-built *Conch* and *Patella* introduced the system of summer tanks, together with very elaborate ventilation for the carriage of benzine; the former system becoming the general rule for a period of nearly twenty years.

It was in this period, too, that the ever enterprising Nobel Brothers introduced the first diesel-driven tankers and the Shell concern commissioned the *Vulcanus*, the first sea-going motor tanker. She was followed not long after by the first German one, the 5,000-ton *Hagen*, which was launched in 1912 and commissioned a year later by the German-American Petroleum Co. The period just before the outbreak of war saw the building of a number of outsize tankers both by this firm and the Eagle Oil.

Then, as now, there was the need for specialised tankers designed to meet local requirements and in 1899 two interesting examples were built on

The Irish American Oil Co.'s s.s. *Queen Maeve*, 4,634 tons gross, whose career is referred to on page 54. She operated under this name from 1924 to 1931, when she was sold for further trading under the Greek flag, first under the ownership of John A. Galani & Co., Istanbul, and then the S. A. Hellenique Maritime & Commercial Transpetrol, of Piraeus. Length 365.1 ft., breadth 50.1 ft. D.w. tonnage 6,775.

The s.s. *Whittier*, an early American tanker owned by the Union Oil Co., San Francisco. She was delivered in 1907 by what is now part of the Bethlehem Pacific Coast Steel Corporation, Shipbuilding Division. She measured 250 ft. 7 in. o.a. length by 31 ft. 9 in. mld. breadth, and had a displacement of 2,660 tons. Reciprocating machinery of 800 s.h.p. gave a speed of 10 knots.

The *Vulcanus*, 1,179 tons gross, length 195.7 ft., breadth 37.7 ft. Built 1911 by the Netherland S.B. Co., Amsterdam, for the Nederlandsche Indische Tankstoomboot Mij., part of the Shell-Royal Dutch Group, she was the world's first full powered ocean-going motor ship. One 6-cylinder 4-stroke S.A. Werkspoor engine gave a speed of 7 knots. She was broken up in 1931.

the Forth by the Grangemouth Dockyard Co. Ltd. to the order of the Burmah Oil Co. These were the little *Syriam* and *Kokine*, both ships of 1,427 tons gross and measuring 235 ft. by 36 ft. Intended for the Indian trade, they incorporated a number of unusual features. Besides the oil compartments there were holds for the carriage of case oil or dry cargo. The ships were also fitted with portable ceiling and sparring, as well as steam pipe lines to clean the tanks and as a protection against fire. The hatches were so constructed that when general cargo was carried, the usual oil-tight hatch could be removed and the whole width of the lower hatch made available. Each vessel had two cargo pumps, together capable of handling 360 tons per hour. The *Kokine* was lost on her first trip, but the *Syriam* had a long and successful career.

A larger tanker, of very different design and appearance, which was built in 1903 at Greenock by the Grangemouth & Greenock Dockyard Co. Ltd., was the *Pennoil*, a ship of 4,434 tons gross, ordered by the Pennsylvania Trading Co., of Hamburg. She measured 365.1 ft. in length by 50.1 ft. in breadth and was of three-island type with engines amidships. Her machinery consisted of the usual single triple expansion engine, which was fired by three Scotch boilers. An interesting contemporary reference to the ship runs thus; '. . . a most successful vessel, used by the Pure Oil Company on the Atlantic trade. At Summer Plimsoll she carries 6,775 tons. She has 22 tanks, two pumprooms and powerful steam fans for eliminating dangerous vapours. Fitted with the most complete system of electric light. Overhead trolley railways convey coal to the stokehold from any part of her extensive bunkers (1,500 tons). Steams 11 knots.' How long she kept her trolley railways is not known, but she was converted to oil fuel in 1924. She also became well known on the Atlantic under other names — as the *Gargoyle* of the Vacuum Oil Co., and as the *Oswego* of the Union Petroleum S.S. Co. Inc., of New York.

Her subsequent career was so varied that it is worth recording. In 1924 both she and the only other unit in the Union Petroleum fleet, the *Westwego* a German-built, ex-Rumanian ship, were transferred to the newly-formed Irish-American Oil Co. Ltd., of Dublin, an offshoot of the Anglo-American Oil Co. The *Oswego* became the *Queen Maeve* and her consort the *Queen Tailte*, the two being the first ocean-going tankers to be owned in Eire. In

The s.s. *Paul Paix*, owned by John M. Lennard & Sons Ltd., Middlesbrough, which was the first ship to be constructed on the Isherwood longitudinal system. Built in 1908 by R. Craggs & Sons Ltd., Middlesbrough, she had a gross tonnage of 4,196 (6,400 d.w.) and measured 355.2 ft. by 49.4 ft. During the 'twenties she was sold to H. Kuhnle, of Bergen, who renamed her *Barde*.

the early 'thirties both ships were sold, the *Queen Maeve* going to Greece, then the traditional home of dry cargo ships but not of tankers, and she had the distinction of being the only tanker under that flag. Subsequently she became the first Israeli-owned tanker. They put her under the Panamanian flag but retained the name *Petroil* and she continued to operate as this until June, 1950, when she caught fire off Sete and had to be beached. The fire and resulting explosions caused such damage that she became a constructive total loss. In size and layout she was representative of quite a few tankers built during the period 1902-08, other examples being the *Lutetian*, *Carpathian* (later *British Peer*) and *Roumanian* (later *Norne*), but with the introduction of new systems of framing there was an almost universal return to the more economical engines aft arrangement.

In the year 1908 there were two notable tanker events. One was the completion by the New York S.B. Co. of the *Oklahoma* (5,853 tons), the largest tank steamer yet built in America, and one that was destined to break in two off Sandy Hook six years later. The other was the building of the British tanker *Paul Paix*, a ship of 4,196 tons gross which marked the beginning of a new era of safer and stronger tanker construction.

This vessel, built by Craggs, of Middlesbrough, for John M. Lennard & Sons, was in no way remarkable as regards exterior appearance, but internally the story was very different, for she was the first ship to be built on the Isherwood longitudinal system of framing. In this the normal closely spaced transverse frames are eliminated, the necessary strength being provided by the fitting of a series of far stronger transverse frames at *widely* spaced intervals. These continue round the top sides and bottom of the hull and are slotted to take many closely spaced longitudinal stiffeners. Besides permitting a greater length:depth ratio, the use of this new system reduced hull weight and eased assembly and maintenance. The *Paul Paix* measured

The s.s. *British Duke*, ex *Terek*, 3,710 tons gross, one of the Petroleum S.S. Co.'s fleet which was acquired by the British Tanker Co., soon after the latter's formation. She is shown after the transfer, with the B.T.C.'s original funnel markings, black with red and white bands and white disc bearing the black painted letters 'B.T.C.' The ship, which was built by Laing, of Sunderland, in 1899, measured 335.5 ft. × 45.0 ft. and had a d.w. capacity of 5,700 tons. She was sold to Italian owners in 1930 and renamed *Laura Corrado*.

355.2 ft. in length, had a deadweight capacity of 6,600 tons and carried her cargo in sixteen tanks. Her machinery, which was amidships, comprised a set of quadruple expansion engines of 2,000 i.h.p. and three boilers. These gave her a service speed of about 10 knots—a little above the average for those days.

Just as the new systems of framing marked a great advance in constructional efficiency, so did the introduction of the so-called summer tanks to the efficient carrying of the tanker's liquid cargo. The *Conch* and all Shell tankers which followed had their summer tanks located in the 'tween decks when they extended the full length of the cargo space. They served a dual purpose; one being the reduction of the free surface of the cargo in the main tanks, at the same time providing an adjunct into which cargo could expand when passing from a cold to a hot climate. Equally important was the fact that they could be used to carry surplus cargo when this was of such a light specific gravity that the filling of the main tanks did not fully load the ship, or bring her down to her marks.

This tank layout became the rule until the middle of the 'twenties, when it was abandoned in favour of the present arrangement. In this there are two longitudinal bulkheads extending the full length of the cargo space. Thus each tank is now divided into three compartments: this provides even greater longitudinal strength, permitting the length of tanks to be increased with corresponding reduction in the ship's weight.

Tanker construction had advanced so rapidly that in January, 1907, the Russian tank steamer fleet totalled 136 units, with a carrying capacity of over 140,000 tons. Besides these there were 166 sailing tankers on the Caspian, and some 1,500 bulk oil barges on the Caspian and Volga, bringing

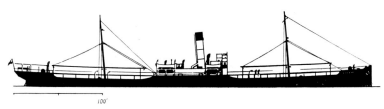

The s.s. *Carpathian* (later *British Peer*), 4,900 tons gross, another of the British Tanker Co.'s early acquisitions. Built by Armstrong Whitworth in 1908, she had a d.w. tonnage of 7,140 and measured 385.0 ft. × 51.0 ft. She is shown with the white, black topped funnel worn when her owners, the Petroleum S.S. Co. Ltd., were controlled by Lane & MacAndrew. She was sold to an Italian firm in 1929 and renamed *Tampico*.

the total capacity to about $3\frac{1}{4}$ million tons. Many of these barges carried as much as 8,000 tons, but the largest at that time was the newly-built *Martha Poseidnetza*, which had been constructed at Torochowitz for D. V. Siritkin, of Nizhni Novgorod. This vessel measured 504 ft. in length, 70 ft. in breadth, 12 ft. 4 in. in depth, had a capacity of about 9,000 tons and was steered by four rudders.

The best known of the early Nobel motor tankers were the *Vandal* and *Sarmat*, which were built on the Volga in 1903-04. Shaped to suit navigation on the Volga and Russian canals, they had a capacity of some 800 tons and were used to take refined products to St. Petersburg. Both ships measured 244 ft. 6 in. in length, 31 ft. 9 in. in breadth and had a load draught of 6 ft. An interesting feature of the *Vandal*'s design was the use of electric transmission from her propelling machinery, which was placed amidships. A much more important pair, however, were the *Emanuel Nobel* and *Karl Hagelin*, which were built for Nobels in 1909-10. The largest units in their fleet, they had a deadweight capacity of over 4,600 tons and were powered by two diesels which developed a total of 1,200 b.h.p. They had turret-shaped hulls, a rather long poop and a sunken fo'c'sle. There were two pole masts, between which was the main mass of superstructure, although the actual navigating bridge was at the break of the fo'c'sle. On the poop there were a couple of small deckhouses but no funnel. Internally, the cargo space comprised seven sets of tanks, subdivided by two longitudinal bulkheads which extended from the forward to the after cofferdam. Accommodation was split up, some in the fo'c'sle and poop, the rest amidships.

Plans to convert their existing tank steamers to diesel-drive were brought to nought by the war and the revolution which followed.

In 1910 Mr. C. Zulver was appointed Marine Superintendent to the Shell fleet. An enthusiast for the oil engine, he began by designing the *Vulcanus*, which was to become the world's first sea-going motor vessel. Built at Amsterdam by the Netherlands Shipbuilding Co., she was of 1,179 tons gross and had a deadweight of 1,194 tons on a draught of 12 ft. 5 in. Her dimensions were 195.7 ft. by 37.7 ft., and she was fitted with a Werkspoor six-cylinder engine of 400 b.h.p. which gave her a speed of 7 knots on a daily fuel consumption of $1\frac{1}{2}$ tons of oil. This engine was the first four-stroke crosshead type ever installed and after the initial difficulties found with all pioneers it proved very satisfactory. The *Vulcanus* was based in the Dutch East Indies and by the time she was scrapped in 1931, the engine was still in perfect running condition, even after it had propelled the ship for over one million miles.

Other pioneer diesel-driven tankers were the Shell owned *Juno* (2,345 tons, built 1912), their larger trio *Artemis*, *Hermes* and *Selene*, all vessels of about 3,700 tons gross, the Belgian (later Russian) owned *Elbruz*, 4,269 tons (the first Tyne-built motor tanker), and the 4,000-ton *Motricine* of 1914, which was the first French one as well as the first to be built there on the Isherwood longitudinal system.

The Eagle Oil Transport Co. came to the fore as tanker owners by building a series of outsize vessels, each of over 17,000 tons deadweight, which made them by far the largest yet in service. These ships came out in 1913-15. Products of various British yards, they varied between 525 ft. and 530 ft. in length b.p., and had a beam of 66 ft. Although only capable of giving a modest 10 knots, their machinery was interesting, for as regards tankers it marked the first large-scale appearance of the quadruple expansion engine.

By the late 'twenties these vessels had become outclassed by newer tonnage. Taking their opportunity, an enterprising Norwegian firm bought one, the *San Gregorio*, and converted her into the whale factory ship *C. A. Larsen*. It was a bold idea, for she was by far the largest in the whaling fleet, but it proved so successful that within a short time four others of these

Eagle tankers, the *San Lorenzo, San Nazario, San Jeronimo* and *San Patricio,* had been bought and altered for this work, becoming the *Ole Wegger, Thorshammer, Southern Empress* and *Southern Princess* respectively. So sound was the construction of these vessels that the *San Gregorio* continued in service until 1954. The other four fell victims to enemy action during the second world war.

Following the delivery of the *Hagen* in 1913, the German-American Petroleum Co. ordered a series of large motor tankers, of a size very similar to that of the Eagle vessels. Probably the best known of these was the *Wilhelm A. Riedemann,* 9,932 tons gross, which measured 525 ft. by 66 ft. A twin-screw flush-decked ship of 15,750 tons deadweight, she was powered by two six-cylinder diesels of 2,800 b.h.p. She was launched by Krupps (who also made her engines) in 1914, but her completion, like that of her consorts, was held up by the war and so it was 1920 before she was finally ready. Even then she ranked as the world's largest motor tanker. For a short while after the war she was named *Zoppot* and flew the flag of Danzig, her owners being the Baltic-American Petroleum Import Co., but she soon reverted to her original name.

An important event which took place in 1915 was the creation of the British Tanker Co. Ltd., which was formed to carry the products of the Anglo-Persian Oil Co., now known as the British Petroleum Co. Ltd. The original nucleus of their fleet consisted of eight ships built during the years 1916-17. The first to be specially designed for the company was the s.s. *British Emperor,* 3,637 tons gross, which was built by Armstrong Whitworth & Co. She had a deadweight tonnage of 5,500, measured 345 ft. by 49 ft. and was fitted with a single triple expansion engine of 1,650 i.h.p. There were seven pairs of main tanks, each with its summer tank above. Forward, there was also a dry cargo hold. During her early life the ship lightered oil cargoes from Abadan over the Shatt-al-Arab Bar, which in those days had not been dredged to its present depth.

The acquisition of the Petroleum S.S. Co. Ltd. in the early days added nine more vessels to the B.T.C. fleet. Growth was rapid and by the end of 1917 the fleet, augmented by other new and purchased ships, had risen to 22. In a number of the old tankers which they bought the engines were

The s.s. *Larchol*, a small Naval tanker built and engined in 1917 by Lobnitz & Co., Renfrew. 1,162 tons gross, 1,520 tons d.w. Dimensions 210 ft. × 34 ft. 6 in. mld. Triple-expansion engines, 700 i.h.p. Still in Admiralty service 1955, together with five others of this class. Note the forward position of bridge and hoses stowed by the low harbour deck.

The *Prestol*, 2,629 tons gross, one of a series of small 14-knot tankers built for the Royal Navy in 1917. Cargo capacity 2,000 tons. Length o.a. 334.7 ft., breadth 41.6 ft. Single-screw triple-expansion machinery, 3,375 i.h.p. Builders: Napier & Miller Ltd., Glasgow. Still in service 1955.

The s.s. *Standard*, 9,725 tons gross, 18,075 tons d.w. Built in 1914 by the Howaldtswerke, Kiel, as the *Jupiter*, she was then one of Germany's largest tankers. She was later operated for many years by the Standard Oil Co. of New Jersey, but is shown in post-war colours when under the ownership of the American European Tanker Co. Inc., of Genoa. A few months later, in 1954, she was sold for scrap. Length o.a. 539 ft., breadth 68.6 mld. Quad.-expansion engines, three Scotch boilers. Speed about 10 knots.

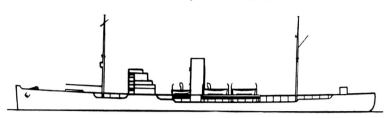

The Admiralty *Leaf* class comprised six vessels: *Appleleaf* (ex *Texol*), *Brambleleaf*, *Cherryleaf*, *Orangeleaf*, *Pearleaf* and *Plumleaf* (ex *Trinol*). Launched by various yards in 1917, they had a length of 405 ft. and a gross tonnage of 5,900. Twin-screw triple-expansion machinery gave them a speed of 14 knots.

amidships, while the officers' accommodation was on a deck immediately on top of the oil cargo tanks. In some instances the valves for these were unwelcome fittings within the cabins! The crew in these ships was berthed forward, in the fo'c'sle.

Compared with the output of dry cargo ships, relatively few tankers were built in Britain during the first world war, and these were mostly designed on very conservative lines. As a result of U-boat losses a great shortage of bulk oil carriers developed and this resulted in a standard design being evolved. Known as the Z type, it had engines amidships, carried a deadweight of 8,000 tons and had a speed of 11 knots. Although some forty were ordered, only a few were ready by the time of the Armistice, when several contracts were cancelled. Of the 34 completed, fifteen were bought by the Admiralty, one was sold to foreign and the rest to British buyers, notably the Anglo-Saxon Petroleum Co. It was also decided to convert a number of the similar sized A and B type dry cargo ships. This retarded their completion by some months and by the end of hostilities only 24 A's and one B type ship had entered service. These were supplemented by a number of old vessels—some of them former passenger liners—which were converted to carry oil in bulk. Amongst these (as described in the last chapter) were many sailing ships which were fitted with either steam or diesel machinery. These were mostly used in the Far East and once the initial shortage had passed were used as oil storage hulks in ports such as Gibraltar, Suez, etc. Another expedient to ease Britain's shortage of oil—conceived by Sir Marcus Samuel and worked out in detail by Mr. C. Zulver—was to adapt the double bottoms and ballast tanks

The *Felania*, 3,882 tons gross, one of the early motor ships of the Shell - Royal Dutch fleet. A twin-screw Werkspoor engined vessel, she was built in 1912 as the *Artemis* by the Netherland Shipbuilding Co., Amsterdam. She was transferred from Dutch to British registry and renamed in 1938. Sold for breaking up in June, 1953. 5,365 tons d.w. Length o.a. 360 ft., breadth 46.7 ft. Speed 9 knots.

The s.s. *Kennebec*, 5,548 tons gross. Built 1919 as the *War Mogul* by R. Duncan & Co., she was one of the standard 'Z' type tankers. Designed to carry heavy fuel oil, the usual summer (side) tanks were eliminated, creating a low harbour deck either side of the central expansion trunk. Owing to this feature the ships were familiarly known as "turrets." Bought by the Anglo-American Oil Co. at the beginning of her career, she remained in their service until her loss—by enemy action—in September, 1939. Length 400.3 ft., breadth 52.2 ft. D.w. tonnage 8,450. Speed 10½ knots.

The s.s. *San Jeronimo*, 12,398 tons gross, one of a group of ten tankers each of 15/16,000 tons d.w. ordered by the Eagle Oil Transport Co. in 1912, and which were the forerunners of the super-tankers of today. The *San Jeronimo* was delivered by Doxfords on 10th February, 1914, and was used during the first war as a Naval base fleet oiler. In May, 1928, she was sold to the Southern Whaling & Sealing Co. Ltd. to become the whale factory ship *Southern Empress*, and as such was torpedoed in the Atlantic on 13th October, 1942. She is seen here leaving San Pedro. Length o.a. 539.2 ft., breadth 66.5 ft. Single-screw quad.-expansion engines.

of other ships so that they could carry oil in these compartments. Altogether over 1,200 vessels were so modified.

Of the various tankers built for the Admiralty, the most notable were the six units of the *Leaf* class (*Appleleaf*, *Brambleleaf*, etc.). Twin-screw ships of about 5,900 tons gross, they had their triple expansion engines amidships, and measured 405 ft. in length b.p. by 54 ft. 9 in. breadth. They were intended not so much for fleet use as to transport oil across the Atlantic and had a speed of 15 knots or more. Another group of smaller sized 14-knot vessels which were designed for fleet work were launched by various British shipyards in 1917. These were given names ending in 'ol,' such as *Prestol*, *Rapidol*, etc., and also had their engines amidships. They measured 335 ft. by 41 ft. 6 in. and had a capacity of about 2,000 tons.

There were also over a dozen smaller units—such as the *Larchol* (illustrated)—which were designed for local and harbour duties. These vessels had their engines aft, but their most unusual feature was the placing of the bridge right forward, on the fo'c'sle. Between this and the poop there was a long trunk deck, some two-thirds the width of the hull, flanked each side by a long, low deck known as a harbour deck.

It was during these war years that the first unit of the now vast Norwegian motor tanker fleet entered service. This was the *Hamlet* (ex *Varjag*), 5,069 tons gross, which was built in 1915 by Gotaverken. Her builders' first motor tanker, she measured 355 ft. in length and 55 ft. in breadth, and was propelled by a pair of two-stroke S.A. Polar type diesel engines of 3,200 b.h.p. After many year's service with Bruusgaard, Koisterud & Co., she was sold to another Drammen firm, that of A/S Prebensen's Tankrederi, in 1937, and renamed *Credo* From 1940 to 1947 she continued under the Norwegian flag, but as the *Realf II*: then sold to Italy she became first the *Ariete* and then the *Sabotino*. It was not till the spring of 1955 that this remarkable ship was finally broken up.

As a contrast to the present times it is interesting to note that seven years elapsed before Gotaverken built their next motor tanker. This was the *Oljaren*, for the Transatlantic S.S. Co., of Gothenburg.

6

The 'Twenties and 'Thirties

AFTER the first world war there was much leeway to make up as regards the rebuilding of the British tanker fleet. As home yards were already busy it was some time before the various tanker companies could begin to meet their needs. The Eagle Oil Co. was one of the first away, for starting with the *San Florentino* of 1919, they were able to add six 18,000-tonners to their fleet. Generally similar to the earlier group of ten, they differed in being turbine-driven. For their eight smaller ships they had to go to the States: this lead was followed by the Anglo-Saxon, which ordered four *Acardo* class vessels (8,000 tons deadweight) from San Francisco builders, and the similar sized *Paludina* class from Hong Kong. For the rest, the Anglo-Saxon had to buy what it could, including a number of standard tankers from the Government. Most curious of their purchases were a number of small monitors, which had been built for the Royal Navy for the purpose of bombarding the Belgian coast. Reconstructed, they made quite satisfactory shallow draught tankers for the Venezuelan area.

Among the technical improvements introduced in the Shell fleet in 1923 was the abolition of summer tanks and the substitution of two longitudinal bulkheads right through the tank section. This brought greater flexibility in dealing with mixed cargoes, reduced costs and improved stability. This arrangement, it should be noted, was also adopted in the *Hamlet*, Norway's pioneer motor tanker which was built in 1915, as well as in one much earlier Tyne-built ship.

Harland & Wolff used material which had been collected for the construction of N class fabricated ships and with it built a series of tankers for the British-Mexican Petroleum Co. Ltd., a firm then managed by

The s.s. *Invergarry*, 6,907 tons gross. One of a series of seven tankers of unique appearance which were built by Harland & Wolff, Belfast, for the British-Mexican Petroleum Co. during the years 1921-4. She had a d.w. tonnage of 10,350 and carried her cargo in a series of cylindrical tanks which were fitted with centreline wash-bulkheads. The *Invergarry* differed from her sisters in having an extra pair of kingposts aft of the funnel.

A. Weir & Co. The first of these was the 6,958-ton *Inverleith*, built 1921, which was followed by six others, all of which carried their oil cargo in circular tanks. Unusual in appearance, they had engines amidships, almost all of their superstructure forward of the funnel and a vee-shaped transom stern. The British Tanker Co., whose fleet included many old second-hand ships, ordered on a very large scale, contracting for 22 of the *British Ardour* class (turbine-driven ships of 10,000 tons deadweight) besides various others. As a result, by 1924 this fleet totalled some sixty ships of over 50,000 tons deadweight.

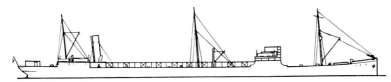

The Standard Oil Co.'s *William Rockefeller* and *John D. Archbold*, both 14,054 tons gross and 22,600 tons d.w., were built in 1921 by the Newport News S.B. & D.D. Co. Two of the largest tankers of their day, they measured 572 ft. 6 in. in overall length by 75 ft. beam. Two sets of triple-expansion engines and three Scotch boilers gave a speed of 10.3 knots. The *William Rockefeller* was torpedoed and sunk near Cape Hatteras in June, 1942, but the other survived the war. Their profile was typical of many of the Company's larger ships built about that time.

In America the many tankers constructed during the war years proved sufficient for immediate needs. The few that were built were of considerably larger size, such as the Standard Oil Co.'s *William Rockefeller* and *John D. Archbold* (both of over 20,000 tons deadweight), and the rather larger *G. Harrison Smith*, built for a Canadian associate, the International Petroleum Co. Another Standard Oil development was the building in 1919-20 of the steam tankers *S. B. Hunt* and *W. J. Hanna*, ships of some 6,800/7,100 tons gross, which were designed to carry refined spirit, a much more dangerous cargo.

The American ferro-concrete tankers *Dinsmore* (illustrated), *Palo Alto* and *Peralta* were built 1920, 1919 and 1921 for the U.S. Shipping Board. They measured 420 ft. b.p. by 54 ft. by 36 ft. and were designed to carry a deadweight of 7,500 tons on a draught of 26 ft. 1½ in. Intended for a speed of 10 knots, they were fitted with single-screw triple-expansion machinery and three Foster White boilers. The *Dinsmore*, which had a gross tonnage of 6,144, was built at Jacksonville, Fla., by A. Bentley & Sons Corp.

This transport of refined products grew immensely in subsequent years, and brought fresh problems, the most important being that of corrosion. This was so serious that it greatly shortened the life of tankers so employed. In 1929 the Anglo-American Oil Co. Ltd. found it necessary to order new centre sections—some 300 ft. long—for their big *Cadillac* and *Saranac*, which were then over eleven years old. The new sections were built by Palmers, Jarrow: when these were ready the ships were withdrawn from service and had their old bow and stern joined on to the new midship section. The old bridge was retained, being transferred bodily to its new base. It was a bold experiment that proved successful, and thanks to careful planning the ships were only out of service for about two months.

Mention must also be made of some little known American experiments in the use of concrete. Most important—on paper—was a trio built in 1919-20-21 for the United States Shipping Board: two, the *Palo Alto* and *Peralta*, on the West Coast, and one, the *Dinsmore*, at Jacksonville, Florida. The largest concrete tankers in the world, they measured 420 ft. in length b.p. and had a deadweight capacity of 7,500 tons. But they were not a success and saw little or no sea-going service.

Another smaller but far more original design was that used for the construction in 1920 of two coastal tankers, the *Durham* and *Darlington*. These ships, each of 2,000 tons deadweight, were built of ferro-concrete by the MacDonald

Section through the American ferro-concrete tanker *Durham*, looking aft, toward the bridge front. She and her sister *Darlington*, both built in 1920, had a gross tonnage of 1,433 and measured 298 ft. in length overall by 33 ft. 9 in. beam. Each was propelled by a pair of Bolinders engines fitted aft. (P denotes central fore and aft passage.)

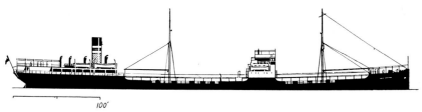

The s.s. *British Advocate*, 6,994 tons gross. One of twenty-two similar turbine driven tankers built 1921-3 for the British Tanker Co. 10,900 tons d.w. on 27.9 ft. draught. Length b.p. 440 ft. × 57 ft. beam.

The twin-screw m.t. *Canadolite*, one of two sisters built in 1926 by Krupps, Kiel, for Imperial Oil Shipping Co. Ltd., a Canadian associate of Standard Oil. Length 510.9 ft., breadth 68.2 ft. 15,600 tons d.w. on 29.2 ft. draught. The *Canadolite*, captured March, 1941, became the German owned *Sudetanland*. As such she was sunk at Brest by the R.A.F. in August, 1944.

The Norwegian m.t. *Turicum*, 7,824 tons gross, 10,600 tons d.w. Built in Holland in 1928 by C. van der Giessen, for Camillo Eitzen & Co., Oslo (Skibs A/S Avanti). Length 451.8 ft., breadth 59.2 ft. One 12-cylinder Werkspoor engine, 4,280 i.h.p. In 1951 she became the Italian owned *Punta Aspra*.

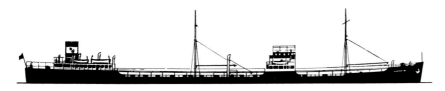

The Norwegian m.t. *Krossfonn*, 9,323 tons gross, built 1935 by the Odense Shipyard for Sigval Bergesen, Stavanger. She was captured by the Germans during the early part of the war and became the supply ship *Spichern*. 14,225 tons d.w. Ten centre and ten side tanks. Length overall 495 ft., breadth 65 ft. Two 7-cylinder B. & W. diesels, 4,800 b.h.p. Speed 13 knots.

Engineering Co., of Port Aransas, for transporting oil to Tampico. In elevation they rather resembled whaleback ships, but had a vertical stem and short, high fo'c'sle with the foremast stepped at the break. Amidships there was a rather large bridge, while right aft there was a short engine casing with a tall, thin funnel placed just astern of the mainmast. The stern was of the vertical barge type, with projecting rudder. But in section these vessels were completely unique. Apart from the bow and stern, which were cast *in situ*, the ships were made up of a series of horizontal units, each 30 ft. long, individual sections being in the form of two intersecting cylinders. Each of these cylinders was built on end (vertically) and later transported to the slip and joined on. The space caused by the intersection of the two cylinders extended the whole length of the cargo space and was used as a communication passage. Oil ducts were provided beneath this and it was by means of these that the cargo was pumped out. The ships were powered by two 160 h.p. Bolinders semi-diesel engines, steam being provided by a 125 h.p. donkey boiler. They were built to the order of the France & Canada Oil Transport Co., of Delaware. Beyond the fact that the *Durham* featured in Lloyd's Register for a number of years nothing is known of their subsequent careers.

Turning again to Great Britain, the motor tanker developed relatively slowly. The Anglo-American built their first, the *Narraganset* and *Seminole*, in 1920-21. Ships of 10,000 tons deadweight, they were fitted with twin-screw four-cycle airless injection machinery made by the hull builders, Vickers Ltd., of Barrow. This firm also built and engined several rather larger vessels for Tankers Ltd. In 1924 the British Tanker Co. received their first diesel-driven tankers, the *British Aviator* and *British Motorist*, which were built by Palmers and Swan Hunter respectively. For the sake of experiment these two were fitted with different types of machinery.

The Standard Oil Co. and its various associates went in for the diesel engine on such a large scale that by the end of 1926 they owned by far the greatest diesel-driven fleet in the world, comprising over two dozen units of more than 300,000 tons carrying capacity. With one exception all their new diesel-driven tonnage was built in Germany, the largest block comprising eleven of a standard 11-knot, 12,000-ton deadweight type, of which

Top left: The Norwegian 9,721-ton m.t. *Jaguar*, after breaking in two during a mid-Atlantic gale while on voyage from Mexico to Germany in January, 1939. The forepart sank later, after the captain and five others had been rescued, but the stern half was eventually towed to Holland, where a new forepart was built and joined on. The ship returned to service as the *Janko* just under a year later. The *Jaguar* was previously the Swedish owned *Nike*, a vessel built by Gotaverken in 1928.

Top right: The Panamanian registered *Nayade*, 8,890 tons gross, one of two pioneer diesel-electric tankers owned by a Swiss firm, the Soc. Anon. Maritime et Commerciale, of Geneva. Built by Scotts, of Greenock, in 1931, as the *Permian*, she became the *Atlantic Belgium* in 1947, receiving her present name after purchase in 1950. Her sister *Brunswick* was also then acquired by this firm and is now the *Driade*. Length b.p. 471.1 ft., breadth 63.3 ft. Note the many exhausts and bridge placed aft, on the poop.

Left: The s.s. *Inverleith*, the first of seven similar ships built 1921-4 for the British-Mexican Petroleum Co. Ltd. by Harland & Wolff Ltd., Belfast. 10,350 tons d.w. Length b.p. 412.6 ft., breadth 55.8 ft. Triple-expansion machinery. In both hull dimensions and shape of stern these vessels resembled the prefabricated 'N' class dry cargo ships.

the *Den Haag* and *Persephone* were examples. The two Krupp-built sisters *Montrolite* and *Canadolite* of 1926 were rather larger, but of generally the same layout, with raised fo'c'sle and bridge, but no island aft. The exception mentioned was the French-owned *General Gassouin*, 5,158 tons gross, which was designed to transport motor lubricating oils of various grades. She had a pair of normally shaped tanks forward, as aft, but she carried the bulk of her cargo in seven pairs of cylindrical tanks.

Besides the normal building programmes of the various oil companies, a number of interesting specialist craft were also built. Probably the most numerous were those for the United Molasses Co., vessels specially designed to handle sugar molasses, a cargo which is particularly heavy and requires extra heating. Even more elaborate equipment was needed for several asphalt carriers, the *Arthur W. Sewall*, *Stanasphalt* and *Ebano*, which came out in 1928-29-30. The successful conversion of the Eagle Oil tanker *San Gregorio* into the whale factory ship *C. A. Larsen* resulted in a series of further conversions of a similar nature and then, in 1929, the building of the *Tafelberg*, 13,640 tons gross, which was the first whale factory ship to be specially designed as such. Further reference to specialist types, including the combined oil/ore carriers, is made in another chapter.

After the initial rush to replace war losses and out-worn tonnage had passed, more attention was paid to the design of tankers, and in particular to their hull lines. The year 1925 saw the introduction of the Isherwood Bracketless system, which was first applied to the 7,101-ton *British Inventor*, which was built by Palmers a year later. This system did not pretend to save weight, but it greatly reduced maintenance costs and eased construction. At the same time it also reduced vibration. Another system was the combination of transverse and longitudinal framing, which appeared in 1926 and reduced the hull weight very considerably.

The counter stern gave way to the cruiser and the stem lost its abrupt vertical character and became raked. The Maierform hull made its debut, but did not catch on with tanker owners in Britain, instead proving more popular for Continental dry-cargo ships. During the middle 'thirties more attention began to be paid to streamlining and in this Scandinavian owners

The s.s. *Esso Dublin*, 7,473 tons gross, a typical steam tanker of the 'twenties and early 'thirties. Originally the *Beaconstreet* of the Beacon Transport Co. of Canada Ltd., she was built by Palmers in 1930. Renamed in 1950 after her transfer to the Anglo-American Oil Co. (now Esso), she was sold to British breakers in November, 1953. Length 450.3 ft., breadth 59.7 ft. D.w. tonnage 12,335. Triple-expansion engines, speed 10 knots.

The m.t. *British Aviator*, 6,998 tons gross. Built by Palmers Co. Ltd. in 1924, she was the first of the British Tanker fleet to be fitted with diesel machinery. This was a 4-cylinder Doxford unit of 2,600 b.h.p. which gave a speed of 10 knots. She was followed shortly after by the *British Motorist*, which was similar but fitted with a Neptune type engine. 10,762 tons d.w. Length 439.8 ft., breadth 57.1 ft. Sold for scrap October, 1953.

The m.t. *Trocas*, 7,382 tons gross, completed in 1927 by the Rotterdam D.D. Co., was one of a group of twelve sisters built by various yards for the Shell fleet. Shortly before the war their Werkspoor type engines were modified and given continuous supercharge, which increased their speed by a knot—to just under 12 knots. D.w. tonnage 10,742. Length overall 456.6 ft., breadth 59.5 ft.

set the pace, although one Dutch firm produced some extreme but unlovely designs.

The International Load Line Convention of 1930 resulted in the deeper loading of tankers. This had a very considerable effect on their earning power, for it permitted a vessel of 12,000 tons deadweight, for example, to load fifteen inches below her old marks. Hitherto American vessels had not been subjected to regulations and had usually loaded considerably deeper than those owned in Britain.

In 1925, an American firm, the Atlantic Refining Co., which had become interested in the possibilities of electricity, had the *Allentown*, a U.S. war-built standard tanker, converted from geared turbine to diesel-electric drive. The results were such that several of their other units were similarly altered. Then, in 1928, they took delivery of the *Brunswick*, 8,947 tons gross, notable as the first diesel-electric tanker to be built in Britain. Her builders were Scotts, of Greenock, whose first tanker had been the famous *Narraganset* of 1903. The *Brunswick* measured 471.1 ft. by 63.3 ft. and was of unusual appearance, for she had all of her accommodation placed aft, while instead of a funnel she had a fistful of thin exhausts. Between the superstructure aft and the fo'c'sle there was a long unbroken deck, beneath which were nine pairs of main tanks besides the usual summer ones. The ship was propelled by four Ingersoll-Rand type diesels which were connected to a single propelling motor, and these gave her a speed of 10 knots at 2,300 b.h.p.

Later, in 1930 and 1931, the *Brunswick* was joined by two others of similar layout. These, which were also built by Scotts, were the rather smaller *Winkler*, 6,927 tons gross, and the *Permian*, which was a repeat of the first vessel. Another of this company's ships, the *J. W. Van Dyke*, of 1939, made history in being the first large tanker to be fitted with turbo-electric machinery. Built by the Sun S.B. & D.D. Co., of Chester, Pa., she had a gross tonnage of 11,651 and an overall length of 542 ft. Her Babcock & Wilcox watertube boilers were provided with automatic combustion and superheat control, while the steam pressure of 625 lb. and temperature of 832 degrees F. were the highest yet used on any American ship. Her service

The t.s.s. *Brigida*, 2,609 tons gross, a shallow-draught tanker built in 1927 for Lake Maracaibo service. Owned by the N.V. Curacaosche Scheepv. Maats., she is one of many similar ships to be found in the Shell fleet. Length 305 ft., breadth 50.2 ft. D.w. capacity 3,154 tons on 13 ft. 7 in. draught. Triple-expansion engines, speed 8 knots.

The m.t. *Yenangyaung*, of the Burmah Oil Co. (Tankers) Ltd. She was built in 1937 by Swan, Hunter, & Wigham Richardson and fitted with Doxford type machinery. The picture shows her after being lengthened in 1953, when an extra 30-ft. section had been added amidships, which increased her overall length to 430.7 ft. and d.w. capacity from 8,000 to 8,700 tons. Gross tonnage now 5,948. Speed about 12½ knots.

The m.t. *Mosli*, 8,291 tons gross, which was the first tanker to have a Maierform hull. Built by Eriksbergs M.V. in 1935, she was owned until 1951 by T. Mosvold, of Farsund, Norway. She then became the *Smeralda* of the Italian Citmar Company. Length 476.8 ft., breadth 68.2 ft. One 6-cylinder B. & W. type engine, 3,500 b.h.p.

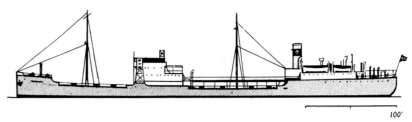

The Dutch built, Norwegian owned m.t. *Buccaneer*, 6,222 tons gross. Built as the *Duivendrecht* in 1929 by the New Waterway S.B. Co. for Phs. Van Ommeren & Co., Rotterdam, she was sold in the middle 'thirties to A.O. Andersen & Co., Oslo and sunk by enemy action in the spring of 1942. 9,525 tons d.w. Length 403.4 ft., breadth 55.2 ft. One Harland-B. & W. 8-cylinder diesel, 2,500 b.h.p. This style of streamlined bridge is seen further developed in the *Bacchus*, *Pendrecht*, etc.

speed was $13\frac{1}{2}$ knots. Later this ship was to serve as the prototype for many of the U.S. war-built tankers.

Cornelius Zulver, who had been responsible for the first sea-going motor tanker, the *Vulcanus*, was also the prime mover in the development of continuous supercharge. The Royal Dutch m.t. *Megara* was a pioneer in this respect, being the first to be built with continuously supercharged diesels. This gave an increase of some 40 per cent. in power without any corresponding increase in size or weight.

Before the war Norwegian owners possessed hardly any tanker tonnage, concentrating instead on dry-cargo carriers. A new phase, however, started in 1925 when they bought over twenty of the Anglo-Saxon's older units, chartering them back to the firm for a period of ten years. In that year Norway owned just under 170,000 tons of tankers, yet during the ensuing ten years her interest in this trade was so great that by 1935 she possessed over 1,300,000 tons.

An important feature of Norwegian ownership is that it is far less centralised than with most other nations. There is thus a greater proportion of owners in outlying ports—often mere villages—whose fleets may total three or four units apiece. These, if tankers, are built for charter work and are very seldom seen in home waters. Another interesting feature has been the readiness of these owners to accept standardised types. This has resulted in the building of a large number of virtually identical ships, nearly all of which have been for different owners.

An early example of this was seen in a medium-sized design of the late 'twenties, from which over a period of five years Gotaverken & Eriksbergs

The Russian m.t. *Kreml*, 7,661 tons gross. Built 1932 by the States S.B. Yard 'Marti,' Nicolaieff, as the *Soyuz Vodnikov S.S.S.R.*, she was given her present name in 1938. 10,800 tons d.w. Length b.p. 446 ft., breadth mld. 56 ft. Engines: two Russian-built 4-cylinder 2-stroke S.A. diesels.

The m.t. *General Gassouin*, 5,158 tons gross, was designed to carry lubricating oils in seven pairs of circular tanks. She was built at Bordeaux in 1926 for the Soc. Auxiliare de Transports, with dimensions 383.7 ft. × 52 6 ft After the war she was rebuilt, given Fiat instead of Sulzer type machinery and became the *Esso Guyenne* of the Esso Standard Soc. Anon. Francaise.

The twin-screw Norwegian m.t. *Vav*, 6,414 tons gross, one of a Scandinavian standard type very popular in the early 'thirties. Built by Eriksbergs M.V., Gothenburg, in 1931, for Halfdan Ditlev-Simonsen & Co., Oslo. 9,835 tons d.w. Length b.p. 408.6 ft., breadth 55.3 ft. Two 6-cylinder B. & W. diesels, 2,300 b.h.p. Speed 10 knots. Sold for scrap 1955.

built nearly a score of ships. The *Vav*, an example of these, measured 422 ft. in length overall by 55 ft. beam, and had a deadweight capacity of 9,000 tons. Twin-screw B. & W. type machinery gave her a speed of 11 knots.

Ten years later Scandinavian owners were thinking in terms of larger and faster ships and one of the well-known designs of the late 'thirties was that brought out by the Deutsche Werft in 1935—a 13-knot ship with a deadweight tonnage of 14,800. It proved very popular with Norwegian owners and vessels of this series were still being turned out in 1939, by which time seventeen had been built by the Deutsche Werft and four by the Bremer Vulkan. They had a streamlined superstructure and three-island type hull, of which the under-water portion was built to a patented shape. They had a dry cargo hold forward, nine sets of tanks and midship pumproom, the top of which was just abaft the bridge. The ships had two longitudinal bulkheads and were propelled by a single diesel engine of 4,100 b.h.p. Today a speed of 13 knots does not seem at all remarkable, but in 1937 the loaded trial speed of 14.8 knots achieved by the *Petrofina* was considered a record for European-owned tankers.

The use of welding is now so general that one is apt to forget that the first all-welded tanker—the *Moira*, 1,560 tons gross—was only built in 1935. Norwegian-owned, she was built by Swan Hunters and measured 248 ft. in length. Another larger ship which aroused considerable interest was the *G. S. Walden*, 10,627 tons gross, which came from a Dutch yard in 1935. She was the first tanker to be built on the new Isherwood arc-form of hull construction, although some years earlier three dry-cargo carrying tramps had been constructed on these lines. As a means of comparison, another ship, the *W. B. Walker*, was also built—on conventional lines—with similar power machinery and designed to carry the same deadweight on an equal draught. Both hulls were of equal length, but the arc-form vessel had nearly six feet more beam and proved to be about half a knot faster. The idea appealed to American owners and a number of their tankers were built on these lines.

It was Japan that set the pace for speed and in 1931 her first fast tanker, the *Teiyo Maru*, 9,850 tons gross, startled the commercial world by attaining a mean speed of 17.53 knots on the measured mile—in ballast, it should be noted. Some years later it was claimed by a Japanese writer that she and other fast tankers had justified themselves commercially: that their operating differential had been made up by the high freights which they could obtain for raw silk, as well as special fish and vegetable oils, on what would have otherwise been empty eastbound Pacific crossings. Subsequently the Japanese Navy became interested and granted subsidies, although a trial speed of at least 19 knots was stipulated. This figure, however, was seldom if ever repeated by the ships in later life.

Between then and 1939 some twenty high-speed tankers were built, of which the sisters *Tatekawa Maru* and *Nippon Maru* were perhaps the most notable. These, which were built in 1935-36, had a deadweight of 13,600 tons, and were owned by the Kawasaki K.K. and Yamashita K.K. respectively. Both were designed for a normal cruising speed of $17\frac{1}{2}$ knots and even at this figure were credited with an endurance of 21,000 miles. Actually, on trial the *Tatekawa Maru* attained 20.5 knots, a record, even for Japan. Among the most powerful single-screw motorships afloat, they were powered by double-acting two-stroke machinery of 9,000 b.h.p., and measured 524 ft. in overall length by 65 ft. beam. The ships had the usual two longitudinal bulkheads and six sets of tanks, making eighteen in all. Besides these there was a dry-cargo hold forward, with 'tween deck space. The pumproom, which was on the centreline amidships, had four pumps for handling heavy oil and one for gasoline. Aft, the *Tatekawa Maru* was fitted with a pair of very tall tripod kingposts, designed to aid the refuelling of naval craft at sea.

American owners in past years had been content with relatively modest speeds and had shown comparatively little interest in the diesel engine. Instead they preferred to use geared turbines, taking high pressure, high temperature steam from watertube boilers, the result being a considerable saving in weight. In 1934 several of their tankers were built with a new and more compact machinery layout, one in which the boilers were placed on a higher level, abaft the turbines. This arrangement was widely adopted in later years—on both sides of the Atlantic.

The building of the fast Japanese tankers had a profound and lasting effect on U.S. tanker speeds. One of the first results was the signing of an agreement between the U.S. Navy and the Standard Oil Co., of New Jersey, under which the latter agreed to build a dozen high-speed tankers specially suited for naval requirements, the extra cost being borne by the Treasury. The first of these, the *Cimarron*, was completed in 1939. A ship of 18,300 tons deadweight, she measured 553 ft. by 75 ft., and had a speed of some 17 knots in service. Subsequently she and the rest of her class were taken over by the U.S. Navy and were converted into escort aircraft carriers, their place being taken by a later and larger fleet of tankers of similar calibre.

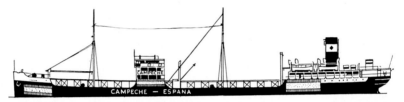

The Spanish m.t. *Campeche*, 6,382 tons gross, which was built at Cadiz, 1934, by the Soc. Espanola de Const. Naval, for the Cia. Arrendataria del Monopolio de Petroleos S.A. Length b.p. 405.5 ft., breadth 57.7 ft. Twin-screw; two 4-cylinder Sulzer diesels, 3,200 b.h.p. Sister ship: *Campomanes*. Vessel shown wearing wartime neutral markings.

7

Standard Tankers of The Second World War

DURING the first half of World War Two the tankers built in the United Kingdom conformed to the pattern of several peacetime prototypes, ones which had proved themselves successful and with which builders were familiar. Most important of these was a Shell design, a motor vessel of 12,000 tons deadweight which, on a fuel consumption of about 12 tons of oil per day could maintain a service of about 12 knots. It was thus familiarly known as the 'Three Twelves,' or sometimes as the 'Ocean.' A typical example measured 460 ft. in length b.p. by 59 ft. breadth moulded, by 34 ft. depth moulded, had a gross tonnage of some 8,280 and a load draught of approximately 28 ft. The aim was to give them single-screw diesel machinery with a couple of Scotch boilers for auxiliary purposes. Owing, however, to the loss of a partial supply of engine forgings from the Continent it was frequently found necessary to substitute triple expansion reheat machinery of 3,800 i.h.p.

The internal layout of these ships was straightforward, there being nine sets of tanks—subdivided by two longitudinal bulkheads to make a total of

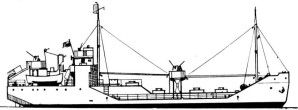

The m.s. *Chant* 4, one of over forty small prefabricated tankers built 1944 to supply the Allied Invasion Forces, which were designed to carry spirit either in bulk or cans. Another twenty-five were completed as dry cargo carriers. All were of a straight line design, which apart from the skeg had no twisted plates. To ease construction each hull was composed of twenty-eight units which were made by inland factories and assembled by various shipyards. (See also page 86.)

The m.s. *Navicella*, a Shell-owned standard type tanker of some 12,000 tons d.w. which was built and engined by Hawthorn Leslie in 1944. Dimensions 483.3 ft. o.a. by 59.2 ft. Gross tonnage 8,255. Speed 12 knots. Note the extra kingposts fitted to handle the A.N.D. (Admiralty Net Defence) booms. Compare with *British Might* below.

The m.s. *British Might*, 8,245 tons gross, a war designed tanker delivered to the British Tanker Co. Ltd. in 1945, by Harland & Wolff Ltd., Glasgow. Length o.a. 484.0 ft., breadth 59.5 ft. One 6-cylinder Harland-B. & W. type diesel, speed 12 knots. Compare with *Navicella* above.

The m.t. *British Drummer*, 3,758 tons gross, one of the twelve 'Intermediate' standard tankers, all of which were built at Sunderland. She was built in 1945 as the *Empire Ensign* by J. L. Thompson & Sons Ltd. and is one of two of this type owned by the British Tanker Co. Ltd. She has a d.w. tonnage of 5,143, measures 357.6 ft. o.a. and has a breadth of 48.3 ft. Compare with *Bursa*, page 92.

The Royal Fleet Auxiliary *Wave Sovereign*, 8,332 tons gross. Built for the Admiralty in 1946 by the Furness S.B. Co. Ltd. Length o.a. 491 ft., breadth 74 ft. 11,835 tons d.w. Single-screw D.R. geared turbines, 6,800 s.h.p., two Babcock & Wilcox boilers. Service speed 15 knots. She has pronounced knuckle aft, and larger bilge radius than earlier *Wave* ships. Note the special platforms and derrick gear for refuelling at sea. (See also page 133.)

The s.s. *Adna*, 7,231 tons gross, a Canadian built 'Park' type dry cargo ship which was completed as a tanker. Built 1943 as the *Mount Royal Park*, she was renamed *Adna* in 1946 by H. E. Hansen-Tangen, of Kristiansand S., Norway, who kept her until 1954. She was then sold to the Sterling Shipping Co. Ltd., Nassau, and converted into the dry cargo carrier *Sterling Viking*. D.w. tonnage (as tanker) 9,867. Length o a. 441.5 ft., breadth 57.1 ft. Note absence of derricks by masts.

The s.s. *Esso Appalachee*, 9,819 tons gross, owned by the Esso Petroleum Co. Ltd. One of the 'Norwegian' war-time standard type, she was built in 1942 as the *Empire Dickens* by the Furness S.B. Co. Ltd. D.w. tonnage 14,810. Dimensions 503.8 ft. o.a. by 68.3 ft. Triple-expansion engines. Speed 10½ knots. Compare with *British Cavalier*, page 84.

27—and two pump rooms, which divided the cargo space into three sections of equal length. Generally, the engineers were accommodated in the lower bridge, with the deck officers and captain above, while the crew were berthed and had their messrooms in and on the poop.

The vessels of the 'Norwegian' type were larger, but of all tanker types of this period they seemed to show the greatest amount of war-time austerity. Altogether 21 were built, six steamers by the Furness S.B. Co., and the rest, ten steam and five diesel-driven, by Sir James Laing & Sons Ltd., who in 1938 had built the prototypes *Eidanger* and *Sandanger* for the Norwegian firm of H. Westfal Larsen & Co. Inevitably, compared with these, the war-built ships were very starkly finished. Instead of the eleven sets of tanks in the former, their *Empire* successors had but six, one small and five large, although the inconveniently large size of the latter was to some extent offset by the fitting of wash bulkheads.

The bridgehouse, which in the first pair had been completely circular, was shaped more conventionally, but retained its chief recognition feature— the exceptionally tall stanchions (two decks high) which supported the projecting boat deck. The largest British war-time standard tankers, they measured 503 ft. in length o.a. by 68 ft. breadth moulded, by 36 ft. depth moulded. The original pair had diesel machinery of 4,800 b.h.p., which gave a loaded speed of 13 knots. Owing to supply difficulties it proved necessary to fit most of the 'Norwegian' type with a single triple expansion engine of 3,800 i.h.p.—as in the *Oceans*. In some later units it proved possible to provide a 3,300 b.h.p. diesel, and finally in the last ships a larger one of 4,400 b.h.p.

As the machinery position gradually improved, the building of the 'Norwegian' type vessels gave way to others of a new design, known as the 'Standard Fast Tanker.' The ships of this type had a deadweight tonnage of 11,900 and a speed of 15 knots, which enabled them to operate independently of convoys. They measured 465 ft. in length b.p. by 64 ft. breadth moulded by 35 ft. 6 in. depth moulded, and were powered by double-reduction geared turbines and watertube boilers. The latter, which supplied steam at 480 lb. pressure, were in a raised boiler room placed abaft the turbines. Hull construction was eased by making the deck of the midship

The tanker/aircraft-carrier *Empire Mackay* (*above*) in her original guise as a M.A.C. ship and (*below*) after her post-war conversion into a conventional tanker. When conditions on the North Atlantic were at their most serious a number of tankers were converted and others built as merchant aircraft-carriers in an effort to combat the U-boat menace. These served in a dual role, carrying much needed petroleum and providing air cover for convoys. The *Empire Mackay*, built 1943 by Harland & Wolff, Glasgow, as a M.A.C. ship, served as such until the end of the war. Bought by the British Tanker Co., she was renamed *British Swordfish* in 1946. Gross tonnage originally 8,908, now 8,113. Length 463.2 ft., breadth 61.2 ft. Speed 11½ knots.

The m.s. *British Cavalier*, 9,889 tons gross, a 'Norwegian' type standard tanker fitted with wartime dummy funnel amidships. Originally the *Empire Cavalier*, she was built in 1942 by Laing, Sunderland, and fitted with an 8-cylinder Werkspoor type engine. D.w. tonnage 14,856. Length o.a. 503.8 ft., breadth 68.3 ft. Renamed in 1945, after her purchase by the British Tanker Co. Ltd. Compare with *Esso Appalachee*, page 81.

section—from foremast to aft end of poop—parallel to the keel, by the fitting of only six pairs of tanks and a single cargo pump room.

The three types, 'Ocean,' 'Norwegian' and 'Fast,' differed considerably in appearance. The first-named had continuous sheer while the others did not. The fast ones had a longer fo'c'sle and correspondingly shorter fore well deck: they lacked well deck bulwarks and had long angled hances. Many of them also had a knuckle aft. Subsequently all of this rather impressive looking type were bought by the Admiralty and given *Wave* names. Individual ships of these types also varied in appearance owing to different mast/kingpost arrangements, a number, for example, being fitted with three pairs of kingposts and long booms from which anti-torpedo nets were suspended. In an attempt to hide the fact that they were tankers some of the first two types were given a dummy funnel amidships. In these cases a pair of kingposts aft served as exhausts.

Twelve ships of another much smaller type, the 'Intermediate,' were also built by two Wearside firms, Laing and J. L. Thompson. These were 335 ft. long, 48 ft. in beam and had a deadweight capacity of 5,000 tons on a draught of only 21 ft. Only the extreme ends of their hulls had any sheer, while to ease construction still more their decks were given an angled camber, flat transversely over the centre tanks and a flat slope over the wing ones. Beneath, they had five sets of tanks and a midship pumproom. After the war most of these vessels were bought by Shell. Another was sold to Canada, while two joined the British Tanker fleet as the *British Bugler* and *British Drummer*.

Next in size and of different appearance were the *Empire Pym* and her three sisters, *Empires Rosebery*, *Jewel* and *Jumna*, which were of 3,200 tons deadweight and measured 301.8 ft. overall by 48.1 ft. beam. The first-named was built by the Blythswood yard, the other three at Grangemouth. These had a short fo'c'sle and long poop, on which was a conspicuous sidehouse which contained the accommodation for officers and engineers. The bridge was placed well forward and was built on the long trunk which extended from poop to fo'c'sle. There was a hinged mast on the bridge and a stump one further forward, midway between bridge and fo'c'sle. These ships, which had a draught of only 18 ft., were designed to enter the French ports as they were cleared after the Normandy landing, and the *Empire Pym* was, in fact, the first oil tanker to enter Cherbourg after D-day.

A large number of coastal tankers were built, the most important being the twenty-odd units designed for service in the Pacific war area. Following normal practice they had names commencing with the word *Empire*. In most instances the three initial letters of the second word gave indication of their design: thus, *Empire Tedlora* (*T.E.D.*, Tanker, Eastern, Diesel) and *Teslin* (*T.E.S.*, Tanker, Eastern, Steam). Both these types were 201 ft. long o.a., while their beam was 32 ft. and 34 ft. respectively. Distinctive because of their counter sterns were the 23 units of the *Empire Cadet* class, whose prototype was the s.s. *Pass of Balmaha*, built by Blythswood in 1933. These steam-driven vessels were designed as oil or water carriers, had an overall length of 202 ft. and a deadweight capacity of 850 tons.

The 'Chant' type tankers, though smaller, were of particularly interesting design. Diesel-driven craft of 480 tons deadweight, they were intended to carry petrol or oil for the Allied invasion of the Continent and for that purpose were shaped for easy beaching. Their construction was one of great urgency and their parts were mostly produced by about thirty non-shipbuilding firms, assembly being carried out at several different yards; Henry Scarr Ltd., Hessle: the Furness S.B. Co. Ltd., Haverton Hill: John Readhead & Sons, South Shields: the Goole S.B. & R. Co. Ltd., and the Burntisland S.B. Co. Ltd.

These ships, of which over forty were built, had dimensions 148 ft. (o.a.) by 27 ft., the load draught being only 10 ft. The hull was of straight-

The s.s. *Esso Tioga*, 797 tons gross. A coastal tanker of the *Empire Cadet* type, she was built at Grangemouth in 1944 as the *Empire Wrestler*, and acquired by the Anglo-American (now Esso) in 1946. 850 tons d.w., length o.a. 202 ft., breadth 31 ft. Triple-expansion engines, speed 9 knots. Note the foremast is stepped to starboard of the centreline.

The *Chant* 69, a small pre-fabricated motor tanker built at Burntisland in 1944. She, like the rest of this numerous class had a deadweight of 465 tons on dimensions 142 ft. 6 in. b.p. × 27 ft. 1 in. × 10 ft. draught. One Crossley engine of 220 b.h.p. gave a speed of 7½ knots. Note that the small hatch covers (seen open) are mounted on the tops of larger ones. See also page 79.

line form, devoid of sheer and all-welded. It had a trunk deck extending from bridge to fo'c'sle and beneath it were four cargo tanks. Each of these had its small circular oil hatch, mounted on a larger rectangular one, so that the tanks could be used for the carriage of cased oil when required. A single-screw 300 b.h.p. engine gave a speed of 7-8 knots. The rest of Britain's war-built coastal tankers consisted of about a dozen smaller vessels, ranging in size from 288 to 340 tons gross. Finally, a large number of 100-ft. long oil lighters.

The number of tankers built in the United States during the war years was colossal. Of the famous T2 types alone, 525 were constructed, besides

The s.s. *Flandria*, 859 tons gross. Built as the *Empire Boy* at Goole in 1942, she was one of three sisters which served as the prototype for the rather shorter yet more beamy *Empire Ted* and *Tes* classes. Subsequent names: *Doorman*, *Flandria* (1947-51), *Alice*, *Hammonia* and *Petra*. As *Flandria* she was owned by the Verenigde Tankkustvaart N.V., Rotterdam, and used as a wine carrier. Length o.a. 224 ft., breadth 31.4 ft.

The m.s. *Alignity*, 890 tons gross, owned by the Everard Shipping Co. Ltd. Built by A. & J. Inglis as the *Empire Fitzroy* in 1945, she, her three sisters and the *Empire Ted* ships were of similar design. The steam driven *Empire Tes* class differed in having their bridge aft, on the poop. Length o.a. 201 ft., breadth 32 ft. (in some units this was increased to 34 ft.). D.w. tonnage 957. One 4-cylinder Polar diesel, 10 knots.

which there were many smaller types, some designed for the U.S. Maritime Commission, others for the Armed Forces.

The first fast tankers—the units of the *Cimarron* class—built 1939-40 were followed soon after by a very similar group of $16\frac{1}{2}$-knotters built for the *Socony-Vacuum Oil Co. In these, too, a number of defence features were incorporated, the extra cost of which was borne by the Government. The vessels which were built 1941-42 by the Bethlehem Steel Company were named *Corsicana*, *Caddo*, *Calusa*, *Catawba*, *Colina* and *Canostoga*. Later they were absorbed into the U.S. Navy and became the fleet oilers *Kennebec*, *Merrimack*, *Winooski*, *Neosho*, *Kankalee* and *Lackawanna*.

* Now Socony Mobil Oil Co., Inc.

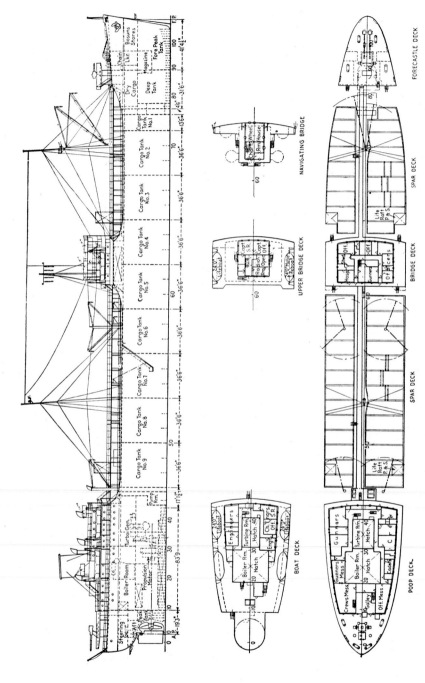

General arrangement of the *James Island*, a typical T2.SE.A1 turbo-electric tanker of which 481 were built during the Second World War in four U.S. shipyards. (Courtesy of *Marine Engineering and Shipping Review*.)

As regards their dimensions—length overall 501 ft. 7 in., breadth moulded 68 ft., depth moulded 37 ft.—they followed the pattern of an earlier Bethlehem-built pair, the *Mobilfuel* and *Mobilube*, which, however, had a service speed of $13\frac{1}{2}$ knots. The 3-knot step-up in speed called for a great increase in the power of the geared turbines—from 4,000 to 12,000 s.h.p.—but this was done with the loss of only one per cent. cargo capacity. The ships had eight sets of tanks with a pumproom aft, beneath the break of the poop. Subsequently many other tankers of generally similar size and power were built for the U.S. Navy.

Although all the tankers of the several T2 designs had identical dimensions, some were given more powerful machinery. The very great majority of them—481 ships—were of the T2-SE-A1 design and these had turbo-electric machinery of 6,000 s.h.p. (7,240 s.h.p. maximum), which gave them a speed of $14\frac{1}{2}$-15 knots. The remaining 44 units, which belonged to the T2-SE-A2 and T2-SE-A3 designs, were fitted with similar type machinery and watertube boilers, but with a normal output of 10,000 s.h.p., which raised the speed to 16 knots.

The four firms responsible for the building of these, the world's largest group of tankers, were the Sun Shipbuilding & Engineering & Dry Dock Co. (198 ships): the Kaiser Co., Swan Island Yard (147): the Alabama Dry Dock & Shipbuilding Co. (102): and the Marinship Corporation (34). The last-named also built the 44 higher powered units, most of which were later taken over by the Navy.

All these vessels measured 523 ft. 6 in. in length overall (503 ft. b.p.) by 68 ft. breadth moulded by 39 ft. 3 in. depth moulded, and had a dead-weight tonnage of 16,800 on a draught of 30 ft. 2 in. Their tank arrangement differed somewhat from the conventional. The forward oil tank was very short—only 13 ft. 6 in. in length—and was divided by only *one* longitudinal bulkhead, while the eight tanks further aft—each 36 ft. 6 in. long—were divided by *two* longitudinals. The main pumproom was right aft and contained three large pumps, each with a capacity of 2,000 gallons per minute, and connected to 200 h.p. motors fitted in the machinery space, which adjoined. Also three smaller cargo stripping pumps, one of 700 and two of 400 gallons per minute capacity. In another pumproom right

The s.s. *Flagship Sinco*, 10,803 tons gross, owned by the Sinclair Refining Co. Inc., New York. Built in 1942 by the Bethlehem Steel Co. S.B. Division, Quincy, Mass. She was one of fifty similar vessels produced by this organization. 17,229 tons d.w. Length o.a. 529 ft., breadth 72.1 ft. Two geared turbines, D.R. geared to a single shaft, 6,600 s.h.p. Speed 14½ knots.

The U.S. naval oiler *Merrimack*, 15,900 tons d.w. Built as the *Caddo* for the Socony-Vacuum Oil Co., she was one of six 16½-knotters built 1941-2 by the Bethlehem Steel Co. Length o.a. 501 ft., beam mld. 68 ft. Geared turbines and watertube boilers, 12,000 s.h.p.

The *White Sands (left)* and *Allatoona*, units of the T2-SE-A1, the world's most numerous tanker type, of which 481 were built by U.S. shipyards. The *Allatoona*, seen with extra wartime aircraft cargo deck, was built in 1945 by the Sun S.B. & Dry Dock Co., Chester, Pa. As the *Jeanny* she was later owned by the North American Shipping & Trading Co. Gross tonnage 10,296, d.w. capacity 16,460 tons. Length o.a. 523.0 ft., breadth 68.2 ft. Turbo-electric machinery, 6,000 s.h.p. Speed 14½ knots.

forward there were two more, of 700 and 300 gallons per minute capacity respectively. Above and slightly forward of this pumproom was a dry-cargo hold with a capacity of 15,200 cu. ft. Although the rest of the officers' accommodation was in the bridge structure, their messroom was at the after end of the poop deckhouse, on the starboard side. That for the crew was on the port side, while the galley which served both was placed between, on the centreline.

Of the U.S. coastal type tankers of this period, the T1-M-BT1 design was one of the largest. Three-island type ships of about 3,150 tons gross, they were rather smaller than the British 'Intermediate' type. The *Tarantella* (now *Stanvac Djirak*), a typical example, built in 1945, measured 327 ft. in length o.a., 48.3 ft. in breadth, and carried a deadweight of 3,933

The twin-screw m.s. *Lac Chambon* (ex *Anticline*), 2,700 tons displacement, a French Naval tanker. One of a series built in the U.S.A. 1944-5, of which three are now with the French Navy. Length 235 ft., breadth 37 ft. Two 5-cylinder Fairbanks-Morse diesels, 1,150 b.h.p., speed 11 knots.

The m.t. *Bursa*, 3,788 tons gross, an 'Intermediate' standard type tanker owned by Shell. Built as the *Empire Crest* in 1944 by Sir James Laing & Sons, she has a d.w. tonnage of 5,168. A single Doxford 3-cylinder engine of 2,400 b.h.p. gives her a speed of 11 knots. Note the retention of the kingposts originally fitted to handle the A.N.D. booms, also the open alleyways beneath the bridge sidehouse — a distinguishing feature of this class.

The m.t. *Punta Loyola*, 3,102 tons gross, owned by the Argentine Government. One of the American T1-M types —comparable to the British 'Intermediate'—she was built 1945 as the *Klickitat* by the Fore River S.B. Co., Jacksonville, Fla., later becoming the *Capitan* before receiving her present name. 4,200 tons d.w. Length 309.1 ft., breadth 47.4 ft. Two 8-cylinder Enterprise engines geared to a single shaft. Note the extension to the original low, wide funnel and the addition of another one at the break of the poop.

tons on a load draught of 19 ft. 1 in. One geared diesel of six-cylinder Nordberg type gave a speed of 10 knots. She had six sets of tanks and was manned by a crew of 34, about ten less than that of T2. Altogether 24 ships of this class were built.

Besides the specially designed tankers many dry-cargo ships of the well-known 'Liberty' type were completed as tankers, their official designation being altered to Z-ET1-S-C3. Sixty-two were completed in this fashion, but within ten years all or nearly all had been converted into dry-cargo carriers.

The Liberty tanker *Eliza Jane Nicholson*, 7,218 tons gross, of the Bernuth Lembcke Co. Inc., New York. She was built 1943 by the Delta S.B. Co. Inc. with triple-expansion machinery giving a speed of 11 knots. Length 422.8 ft., breadth 57.0 ft. D.w. tonnage 10,682. She was transferred to Liberian registry in 1954 and became the *Aetna* of the Alonso Cia. Nav. S.A., Monrovia. She may be distinguished from a Liberty dry cargo carrier by reduced number of derricks and presence of vent pipes up the masts.

8

Post-War Developments

THE post-war years brought many fundamental changes in the oil industry, one being the changed position of the U.S.A., who, owing to vastly increased internal consumption, found herself not so much an exporter but rather an importer of oil. Coinciding with this was the focusing of attention on the Middle Eastern oilfields, which acquired a new and far greater importance as being the most economical source of supply available to Western Europe. The chief handicap was the great distance for the oil haul between well and consumer: from terminals in the Persian Gulf to ports in southern France 4,500 miles, to the English Channel 6,000 miles.

Several pipelines were laid across the desert to ports in the Eastern Mediterranean and these resulted in considerable economies. For example, the trans-Arabian pipeline which was completed in December, 1950, was constructed to carry crude oil from the Saudi Arabian oilfields to Sidon, on the Mediterranean coast. Just over 1,000 miles long, this pipeline shortened by 2,500 miles the distance which oil from the Persian Gulf had to travel to reach Europe. At the time it was estimated that this would save the equivalent of about 62 T2 type tankers. Nor was this all, for it also saved the payment of Suez Canal dues.

Another interesting pipeline constructed was that from Loch Long, on the Firth of Clyde, to the Anglo-Iranian† refinery at Grangemouth, on the Firth of Forth. Loch Long is able to accommodate very large tankers and these are now saved the necessity of travelling round the south and east coasts of England. More than commercial considerations were involved, for this would obviously be of strategic importance in time of war.

Another radical change (probably hastened by the long shut-down of

† Now British Petroleum Co. Ltd.

94

supplies from Abadan, and with it the realisation of the dangers of nationalistic ideas abroad), was the desirability of having refineries near the consumer rather than the producer. As a result the number of new refineries which were needed to meet the great step-up in demand were built in Britain, and to a lesser degree on the Continent, while others, too, were planned for India and Australia.

Thus operations started in 1950 for the building of a Shell refinery at Shell Haven, while a vast one for the Anglo-Iranian† was constructed on the opposite side of the Thames Estuary, on the Isle of Grain. With the completion of their various building programmes the Shell group had major refineries at Stanlow, on the Manchester Ship Canal and at Shell Haven. The Anglo-Iranian had refineries at Llandarcy, in South Wales (served by Swansea): at Grangemouth: and on the Isle of Grain. Two American companies, Caltex and Esso, built theirs on Southampton Water. Besides these there was another refinery at Coryton, on the Thames, owned jointly by Powell Duffryn and the Vacuum Oil Co.

Longer voyages and increased production brought for a while an insistent demand for more tankers, and construction in Britain and on the Continent, in particular, reached new high levels. At this point two new trends gained momentum; one the building of ever faster and larger tankers and the other the eagerness of British tramp shipowners to acquire tanker tonnage. These post-war years also saw the formation in Britain of new tanker fleets, the *Border* ships of The Lowland Tanker Co. Ltd., the eleven *Londons* built for the London & Overseas Freighters Ltd., and the rebuilding of Britain's largest independent tanker fleet—that of Hunting & Son, Ltd., who, while concentrating on vessels of 12,000 to 18,000 tons deadweight, have also ordered one of 31,000 tons deadweight, which at the time of writing has yet to be launched.

Notable among Shell-Royal Dutch achievements were the fitting in 1951 of an experimental gas turbine in the tanker *Auris* (8,221 tons gross), and the immensity of their tanker building programme. Their *Velletia*, which was completed in 1950, was the largest tanker yet built in Britain, her deadweight tonnage being 28,000. Later Shell gave the largest orders ever placed for a group of tankers—as far as the United Kingdom or

† Now British Petroleum Co. Ltd.

95

The Swedish m.t. *Aida*, 9,488 tons gross. Built 1951 by the Caledon S.B. & E. Co. Ltd. for the Rederi A/B Wallenco (Olof Wallenius), Stockholm. Length 492.3 ft., breadth 64.2 ft. D.w. tonnage 13,850. One 4-cylinder Doxford type engine, 5,000 i.h.p., speed 13½ knots.

The m.t. *Regent Tiger*, 9,960 tons gross, which was delivered in October, 1946, to the Bowring S.S. Co. Ltd. by Swan, Hunter, & Wigham Richardson Ltd. She was renamed *Capulet* in 1955, her time charter to the Regent Oil Co. Ltd. having expired. Length o.a. 525.1 ft., breadth 67.3 ft. D.w. tonnage 15,170. One 4-cylinder Doxford type engine, 5,350 b.h.p., speed 11½ knots. The first Bowring tankers, the *Bear Creek* (2,411 tons gross) and *Beacon Light* (2,763 tons gross) were built as far back as 1890.

The m.t. *London Prestige*, 16,194 tons gross, built 1954 by the Furness S.B. Co. Ltd. She and her sister *London Splendour* are the largest of a group of eleven tankers built 1950-4 for the London & Overseas Freighters Ltd. The accommodation is of an exceptionally high standard and each ship, by permission, carries the coat of arms of the City of London on her bridge. D.w. tonnage 24,600. Dimensions 592 ft. (o.a.) × 80 ft., Doxford type machinery, speed 14 knots.

The Italian m.t. *Andromeda*, 12,480 tons gross, owned by the Azienda Generale Italiana Petroli. Built 1952 by the Cantiere Riuniti dell' Adriatico, Trieste. 19,110 tons d.w. Length 541 ft., breadth 73 ft. One 10-cylinder Sulzer type diesel, 8,300 i.h.p., speed 14½ knots. Note the recessed anchor and very clean lines of the streamlined bridge.

The s.s. *Santa Maria*, 11,291 tons gross. Built 1952 by the Bethlehem Sparrows Point Shipyard Inc. for the Figueroa Tanker Corporation, Wilmington (Union Oil Co. of California). Length o.a. 551 ft., breadth mld. 68 ft. D.R. geared turbines, single screw, 7,700 s.h.p. at 95 r.p.m., speed 14 knots. Note the absence of catwalk forward.

The Finnish m.t. *Wiikinki*, 10,388 tons gross, owned by the Suomen Tank-Kilaiva O/Y. Built 1952 by C. Van der Giessen & Zonen, Krimpen a/d Yssel. Length o.a. 522.4 ft., breadth 65.2 ft. One M.A.N. 9-cylinder engine, 6,300 h.p., speed 14½ knots. The largest Finnish owned merchant ship when built, she has a d.w. tonnage of 15,035. There are ten centre and ten wing tanks. Note the forward extension of the poop and the widely spaced stanchions.

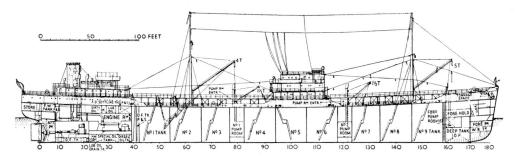

The Shell tanker *Auris*, 8,221 tons gross, which was completed in April, 1948, by R. & W. Hawthorn Leslie & Co. Ltd., Hebburn. She was then a diesel-electric ship, fitted with four 8-cylinder Hawthorn-Sulzer engines, each of 1,100 b.h.p., and coupled to an alternator supplying current to a single propelling motor at 3,750 s.h.p. Later one of these diesels was replaced by a gas turbine of 1,200 b.h.p. In January, 1955, it was announced that the results obtained from this had been so satisfactory that the existing machinery would be replaced by a single gas turbine engine of 5,300 b.h.p. operating through direct gearing. One of the Shell's standard 12,000-ton class, the *Auris* measures 482 ft. in length overall by 59 ft. breadth. She has 9×3 cargo tanks.

Europe were concerned—fifty of a standard general purpose design, each with a deadweight capacity of 18,000 tons.

Abroad, Germany, Italy and Japan started afresh to build up their tanker fleets and produced some very fine ships, while in the United States various new oil companies appeared. But probably more spectacular was the rapid development of three independent tanker fleets—those owned by the Ludwig, Niarchos and Onassis groups of companies. For reasons of economy an ever-growing number of tankers were registered under flags which a decade or two before were virtually unknown at sea—the Panamanian, Liberian, Honduran and Costa Rican.

The end of Soviet participation in the oil trade of Great Britain came in 1948 when the British assets of Russian Oil Products were purchased by the Regent Oil Co. Since its formation in 1924 R.O.P. had been the only importer of Russian oil into this country. Among the big tanker owning firms there were also several changes of name. The long established Anglo-American Oil Co. Ltd. became the Esso Petroleum Co. Ltd., management being vested in the Esso Transportation Co. Ltd. Another, which came into force at the beginning of 1954, concerned the Anglo-Saxon Petroleum Co. Ltd., which then placed the management of their fleet with a newly formed company, Shell Tankers Ltd. Some months later, at the end of

French m.t. *Roussillon*, 11,076 tons gross, launched ready for trials, by the At. & Ch. de la Seine Maritime, Le Trait, 1951. Owners: Soc. Francaise de Transports Petroliers S.A. (S.F.T.P.), Paris. Length 516.3 ft., breadth 70.0 ft. 17,323 tons d.w. One 8-cylinder diesel, speed 13 knots.

The m.t. *Beauce*, 11,742 tons gross, owned by the Soc. Francaise de Transports Petroliers, Paris. Built 1953 by the At. & Ch. de la Seine Maritime, Le Trait. Length 548 ft., breadth 67.5 ft. 17,500 tons d.w. One B. & W. type 8-cylinder engine, 8,400 i.h.p., speed 14 knots. Note the very streamlined bridge.

Dutch m.t. *Pendrecht*, 13,150 tons gross. Built 1953 by Wilton-Fijenoord yard, Schiedam, for N.V. Phs. Van Ommeren. Length 542.0 ft. breadth 74.0 ft. 19,500 tons d.w. One Doxford type engine, 8,000 i.h.p., speed 14½ knots.

The m.t. *Janova*, 12,482 tons gross, built 1953 by Harland & Wolff Ltd., for Anders Jahre & Co. A/S, Sandefjord. (Spermacet Whaling Co. S.A.). Length o.a. 572 ft., breadth 73.3 ft. 19,500 tons d.w. One 6-cylinder Harland-B. & W. engine, 9,200 b.h.p., speed 15 knots.

The Shell tanker *Limatula*, 6,476 tons gross, discharging crude at the Pernis Refinery. Built 1950, by Smith's Dock Co., she is one of a group of twelve sisters built by various yards during the years 1946-50. Length o.a. 446.2 ft., breadth 54.4 ft. One 6-cylinder Werkspoor engine, speed 12 knots. D.w. tonnage 9,445.

The s.s. *Velletia*, 18,661 tons gross. One of four ships, each of 28,000 tons d.w. which were completed 1952 by Swan, Hunter, & Wigham Richardson Ltd. Length o.a. 643 ft., breadth 80 ft. Thirty-three cargo tanks, capacity 26,000 tons. D.R. geared turbines, 13,000 s.h.p. Three watertube boilers, 500 lb. per sq. in., 750 deg. F. Service speed 15 knots. Sisters: *Velutina*, *Verena*, *Volsella*. Shown discharging at Thames Haven.

that year the various tanker companies of the Royal Dutch Shell group whose ships operated under the Dutch flag, put theirs under the management of another new company known as Shell Tankers N.V. Among the firms concerned were the Nederlandsche Indonesische Tankvaart Maats., Petroleum Maats. La Corona N.V. and the Curacaosche Scheepv. Maats., who together operated 56 vessels of 600,000 tons deadweight, not counting a further seventeen which were on order.

Besides the almost universal adoption of welding there followed an appreciation of the greater economies offered by the use of larger and faster tankers, especially for the long regular hauls where deep water terminals were available. In 1949 the completion of the Norwegian m.t. *C. J. Hambro*, a ship of 24,900 tons deadweight, aroused great interest. Apart from one whaler she was the largest oil carrier yet built in the United Kingdom: she was also the first of a long series of similar ships ordered by various firms from the Furness Shipbuilding Co. Ltd.

Among the earlier of these large tankers built on the North-East Coast, the *Rondefjell* attracted particular attention. A ship of 23,000 tons deadweight, she was ordered by Olsen & Ugelstad, of Oslo, from the Wearside firm of John Crown & Sons Ltd., whose largest ship had previously been of only 4,000 tons. As their slips were not capable of building such a great hull in one piece, the *Rondefjell* was constructed in two sections, which were launched as separate units, towed to the Tyne and there joined to form one whole with an overall length of 630 ft.

Once the trend for larger vessels had started the idea continued to gain momentum, and new records for size were continually being established and lost as some yet greater tanker appeared. Besides this there was a growing tendency to use ships for the carriage of cargoes such as chemicals, liquified gases, etc., and also in view of the growing demand for ore carriers to build vessels which could carry ore one way and oil the other. These, like the super tankers, are dealt with in a later chapter.

9

Whalers

THE modern whale factory ship is necessarily large, usually of some 13,000-18,000 tons gross. The lower part of her hull resembles that of the tanker, with the same series of oil tanks, but between these and the long open flensing deck the hull space is occupied by a series of whale oil boilers and elaborate processing equipment. Her accommodation needs to be extensive, for besides the crew normally found in a ship of her size she has also to carry the factory hands and have room for the crews of her catchers. Thus the number carried on a large whaler may total 400 or more. The amount of fresh water required for these and the processing machinery is prodigious and calls for very extensive evaporating plant capable of producing some 700 tons per day.

During the middle of the last century America held the world lead in whaling. In 1846 she owned over 700 whalers and New Bedford was the world's greatest whaling port. But with a growing scarcity of whales and the sinking of the first oil well in 1859, the industry went into a period of eclipse. When interest was gradually revived it was due to the initiative of Norwegians, in particular to that of Svend Foyn, of Tonsberg, who in 1872 was granted exclusive rights to catch whales along the coast of Finnmark. Here he experimented with the shell-harpoon and fitted a harpoon gun in the bows of a small steamer and so created the prototype of the modern whale catcher. The whaling grounds in the Antarctic were opened up from 1905 by the Norwegian pioneers, Captain C. A. Larsen and Commodore Chr. Christensen. Although after the first world war Norway still retained her premier place in the whaling industry, her fleet in 1922—catchers excepted—consisted of only just over a dozen ocean-going units, most of

The Norwegian s.s. *C. A. Larsen*, 13,246 tons gross, which was bought by the Hvalfanger A/S Rosshavet, of Sandefjord, in April, 1926. Formerly the *San Gregorio* of the Eagle Oil Transport Co. Ltd., she was the first large tanker to be converted into a whale factory, and the only one to have her ramp forward. When built by Swan Hunter's in 1913 she was one of the largest tankers afloat. Length 527.2 ft., breadth 66.6 ft. Quad.-exp. engines. Renamed *Antarctic* 1945. Reverted to a tanker 1952. Scrapped in Germany 1954.

them of considerable age, and in size averaging about 4,000 tons gross. Of these, the *Pythia*, owned by the A/S Odd (A/S Thor Dahl), of Sandefjord, was a typical example. A single-screw steamer of 4,401 tons gross, she had been built in 1893 as the *Raglan Castle* to the order of Donald Currie's Castle Line. After various changes of name and service, she was acquired and converted for whaling in 1911.

In 1923-24 Captain Larsen made a trip to the Ross Sea in the *Sir James Clark Ross* (ex *Mahronda*), a ship of 8,224 tons gross, recently bought from the Brocklebank Line, and in those fresh grounds found whales in abundance. The year 1925 brought the revolutionary introduction of the stern ramp, which was first fitted in the 7,866-ton s.s. *Lancing*, another new Norwegian purchase. From that time on expansion was rapid and many more units were bought and converted by Norwegians. Most important of these was the 13,246-ton *C. A. Larsen*, which was acquired in 1926, for this ship, formerly the *San Gregorio* of the Eagle Oil Transport Co., was a tanker, and so the main part of the hull needed little alteration, the factory space being built on top, between the bridge and funnel. The problem of incorporating a stern ramp into a ship which had her engines aft proved daunting, and accordingly this feature was built into the bows. The arrangement did not prove very satisfactory and was not repeated in later ships. Subsequently four other Eagle tankers were bought, to become the Norwegian-owned *Ole Wegger* and *Thorshammer* (the latter still in service), and the British *Southern Empress* and *Southern Princess*, which were operated by the Southern Whaling & Sealing Co. Ltd.—subsidiary of

Lever Bros. Other notable conversions of that period were those of the White Star liners *Athenic, Medic, Runic* and *Suevic*, which became the *Pelagos, Hektoria, New Sevilla* and *Skytteren* respectively. These wonderful old vessels, which had been built by Harland & Wolff, 1899-1901, and had a gross tonnage of around 12,000, were all sunk during the second world war.

The first specially designed whale factory ship was the Swan Hunter-built *Vikingen* of 1929, owned by C. Rasmussen & Co., Sandefjord. A vessel of 14,526 tons gross and 493 ft. in length, she was powered by two sets of triple expansion engines. At the time of writing she is still in service as the Russian-owned *Slava*. She was followed during the next couple of years by several others, rather larger, but of the same general design; the South African owned *Tafelberg*, and the Norwegian *Vestfold, Svend Foyn* and *Sir James Clark Ross (II)*. The last named, which was the first whaler to be fitted with diesel engines, had a gross tonnage of 14,367 and carried a deadweight of 20,300 tons.

The factory ships of the later 'thirties—Japanese included—were built on very similar lines to these, but showed a steady increase in size, reaching a climax in the *Kosmos, Terje Viken* and German-owned *Unitas*. This last ship, which measured 635 ft. long o.a. and had a gross tonnage of 21,846, was later surrendered to become the *Empire Victory* and now operates as the South African-owned *Abraham Larsen*.

By the time the last war was over the whaling fleets were very depleted, yet there was an urgent world-wide need for whale oil. The first of the new building programme to be completed were the four steam-driven ships *Southern Venturer* (14,493 tons gross), *Southern Harvester* (15,448 gross), *Balaena* (15,715 gross), and the Norwegian-owned *Norhval* (13,830 gross), all of which came from British yards. These were followed in 1947-48 by a series of Norwegian diesel-driven vessels, the *Thorshavet, Thorshovdi, Kosmos III* and *Kosmos V*, all of 17,000-19,000 tons. For various reasons the last-named has so far been obliged to operate as a tanker, as has the Argentinian-owned *Cruz Del Sur* (ex *Juan Peron*), 24,570 tons gross, which was built by Harland & Wolff in 1951.

The appearance of the relatively small Dutch-owned *Willem Barendsz*

The Norwegian factory ship *Lancing*, 7,866 tons gross, the first to have a stern ramp. Owners: Hvalfanger A/S Globus (Melsom & Melsom), Nanset. Bought in the 'twenties as *Flackwell*, ex *Calanda*, ex *Omsk*, ex *Rio Tete*, ex *Knight Errant*. Built 1898 for Knight S.S. Co., London, by C. Connell & Co. Dimensions 470.0 ft. × 57.2 ft. Single-screw triple-expansion engines. She was sunk during the Second World War.

The Norwegian s.s. *Ole Wegger* as she appeared after her conversion into a whale factory ship, but before the stern ramp was added. Built by Swan Hunters as the *San Lorenzo*, she was delivered to the Eagle Oil Transport Co. Ltd on 10th February, 1914. Sold to A/S Ornen, of Sandefjord, September, 1928. Captured by German raider 1941. Scuttled by Germans in River Seine 1944. Salvaged later that year by Allies and broken up in Gothenburg 1946. 12,201 tons gross. Length 527.1 ft., breadth 66.6 ft. Quad.-expansion engines.

The s.s. *Southern Princess*, 12,156 tons gross, of the Southern Whaling & Sealing Co. Ltd. Bought May, 1929, as the Eagle tanker *San Patricio*. Built 1915 by Armstrong Whitworth & Co. Ltd. Dimensions 530.6 ft. × 66.6 ft. Quad.-expansion machinery. Torpedoed and sunk March, 1943.

The s.s. *Hektoria*, 13,797 tons gross, a Norwegian factory ship that was formerly the White Star liner *Medic*. Owned by A/S Hektor (N. Bugge), of Tonsberg. Built and engined by Harland & Wolff, Belfast, 1899. Twin-screw quad.-expansion engines. Length 550.2 ft., breadth 63.3 ft. Torpedoed in Atlantic, September, 1942.

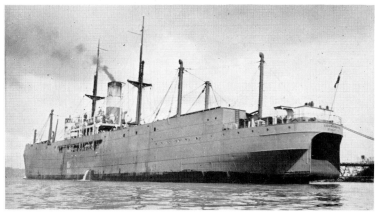

The s.s. *Sourabaya*, 10,107 tons gross, owned by The South Georgia Co. Ltd. (C. Salvesen & Co., Leith). Built 1915 by Workman Clark, as the *Carmarthenshire* for R.M.S.P. sold and converted 1929. Torpedoed October, 1942. Dimensions 470.2 ft. by 58.3 ft. Quad.-expansion engines. Originally of three-island type.

The *Tafelberg*, 13,640 tons gross, one of the earliest of the specially designed whale factory ships. Built 1930 by Armstrong Whitworth for the Kerguelen Sealing & Whaling Co. Ltd., Cape Town. Length 508.3 ft., breadth 72.5 ft. Twin-screw triple-expansion machinery. Differed from most later vessels in being flush decked. Damaged by mine in January, 1941, she was reconstructed as the tanker *Empire Heritage* (15,702 tons gross). Torpedoed and sunk September, 1944.

WHALERS

The Dutch m.s. *Willem Barendsz* (1), 10,635 tons gross, of the Nederlandsche Mij. voor de Valvisvaart N.V. (Vinke & Co.), Amsterdam. Built by Gotaverken in 1931 as the Swedish tanker *Pan Gothia*, she was converted at Amsterdam in 1946 as shown. Later her two forward funnels were heightened. Replaced by a new ship of this name in 1955 (see page 109), she then became the tanker *Bloemendael*. Length o.a. 508.5 ft., breadth 64.2 ft. Two 6-cylinder B. & W. type engines, 4,100 b.h.p.

The m.s. *Thorshavet*, 17,081 tons gross, a post-war factory ship owned by A/S Ornen (A/S Thor Dahl), Sandefjord. Built by Harland & Wolf, 1947. Length o.a. 587.3 ft., breadth 77.3 ft. D.w. tonnage 21,000. Twin-screw. Two 6-cylinder Harland - B. & W. diesels.

The *Cruz Del Sur*, 24,570 tons gross, owned by the Cia. Argentina de Pesca, S.A. Built as the *Juan Peron* by Harland & Wolff in 1951, she was then the world's largest factory ship. She was renamed in the autumn of 1955, following the fall of the Peron regime. D.w. tonnage 26,200. Length o.a. 664.1 ft., breadth 80.3 ft. Twin-screw. Two Harland-B. & W. diesels.

(10,635 tons) was a notable event, for it was a long time since that country had participated in the whaling industry. Formerly the Swedish motor tanker *Pan Gothia*, she was reconstructed at Amsterdam in 1946, and emerged with a unique arrangement of four funnels, set in pairs. This feature was later repeated in the Onassis-owned *Olympic Challenger* (13,019 tons), a former T2 type tanker with turbo-electric machinery which was converted by a German shipyard in 1950.

The *Thorshavet*, completed by Harland & Wolff, of Belfast, in 1947, may be taken as representative of the modern whale factory ship. Built to the order of the A/S Thor Dahl, of Sandefjord, she is a twin-screw motor ship of 17,081 tons gross, carrying a deadweight of approximately 21,000 tons on a mean draught of 34 ft. 6 in. (summer freeboard). She is 587.3 ft. long overall, has a moulded beam of 77 ft. and is 39 ft. 6 in. deep to the factory deck. There are ten main oil cargo tanks, divided by three longitudinal bulkheads, while 2,000 tons of fuel may be carried in the double bottom and deep tanks. The propelling machinery comprises two Harland-B. & W. type six-cylinder S.A. four-cycle diesels with under-cylinder pressure charging. These have a combined output of 7,200 i.h.p. at 110 r.p.m. and give a loaded speed of about 12 knots. In the engine room all the auxiliaries are steam driven, while steam pumps for handling the whale oil cargo are sited in two pumprooms, one placed between Nos. 3 and 4 main tanks and the other between Nos. 7 and 8. For hauling the whales up the slipway there are two 40-ton steam winches, placed on top of the winch-house amidships, while a pair of steam capstans, on top of the after casing, handle the 'scissors' or grab hooks which are fastened to the whale carcase before hauling begins. Besides these a 15-ton steam winch is mounted at the after end of the fo'c'sle. On the flensing deck, which is 291 ft. long, there are four bone saws and a number of steam capstans, which together with the many electric 5-ton cargo winches handle the flensing of the whales. The cut-up portions are then distributed through hatches to the factory boilers below.

The factory plant includes twenty rotating boiler units, an equal number of whale-oil settling tanks and two glue-water plants with vibrating screens. Altogether there are 65 motors here, with an aggregate load of

The world's largest whale factory ship, the *Willem Barendsz (II)*, which was completed in the summer of 1955 by the Dok-en-Werf Wilton-Fijenoord N.V., Schiedam. She has a gross tonnage of 26,830 (44,300 tons displacement) and dimensions 677 ft. 5 in. length o.a., 90 ft. 3 in. breadth mld. and 62 ft. depth mld. Two 6-cylinder M.A.N. type engines of 10,500 b.h.p. give a loaded speed of 14 knots. Her owners are the Nederlandsche Mij. voor de Valvisvaart N.V. (Vinke & Co.), Amsterdam.

The Norwegian factory ship *Norhval* accompanied by her Westland S55 helicopter. This type of machine is proving invaluable for spotting whales. Indeed, the helicopter's slow flying qualities may eventually render it the ideal platform for whale killing, which would be done with the aid of electric harpoons. As may be seen, the hangar and flight deck occupy only a relatively small amount of deck space.

700 k.w. To provide the necessary current the ship is fitted with four 425 k.w., two 100 k.w. and a pair of smaller diesel engined generators, while steam for the auxiliaries and processing plant is supplied by six oil-fired multi-tube boilers. To make it possible to employ the vessel as a tanker outside the whaling season, the factory (336 ft. long) is equipped with mechanical ventilation. Indeed, the ventilation of the entire ship is carried out by means of steam-heated air, which is passed by powerful blowers through ducts to all compartments. Its temperature is automatically regulated by thermostats placed throughout the accommodation.

As regards navigational aids, the *Thorshavet* is fitted with a gyro-compass, echo sounder, electric log and radar. Her crew totals 392, made up of 166 factory workers, 143 catchers' crews and 83 for working the ship herself. Forward there is an electrically equipped laundry, galley and bakery, as well as accommodation for the gunners, deck and engineer officers, together with that for part of the crew, the rest of whom are berthed aft. Cabins for the captain, owners, factory manager, chemist, inspectors, etc., are provided in the bridgehouse.

An interesting development of 1954 was the equipping of the *Southern Harvester* and *Southern Venturer* with a helicopter apiece, for whale spotting. To accommodate the machines the superstructure aft was raised and extended to form a flight deck, while a hangar 50 ft. in length by 19 ft. in height and width was added just abaft the funnels. By using light alloys it was possible to keep the extra weight down to 15 tons.

Today the two largest whale factory ships are the *Willem Barendsz (II)*, 26,830 tons gross, which was completed in the summer of 1955, and the Argentine owned *Cruz Del Sur*, which has a tonnage of 24,570.

10

Harbour, Coastal and River Tankers

THE coastal tanker is a type which before the first world war was virtually unknown in Great Britain. Then the only fleet of any size was that owned by the Anglo-American Oil Co. and which was used to distribute oil from the company's main depots at Purfleet, etc., to their smaller distributing centres around the British Isles. The *Osceola*, typical of their first ships, was built in 1897 and had a deadweight of 380 tons on a load draught of 10 ft. Coming to a rather later period, one of the most important of their vessels was the Grangemouth-built *Tioga* of 1912, a ship which carried some 800 tons on a draught 2 ft. greater.

Even by the late 'twenties there were only a small number of such vessels owned in the U.K., and of these most belonged to the big oil companies rather than independent firms. Of those well known today, F. T. Everard & Sons, in 1929, owned but five coastal tankers, four of them relatively modern and one, the *Alchymist*, a steamer of 382 tons gross which dated back to 1895—one of the pioneers of her type. Now they have some 30 tankers as well as about 60 other ships. In that same year Christopher Rowbotham & Sons, whose fleet now numbers about ten motor tankers, then had but one steamer carrying oil, this being the *Steersman*, 553 tons, which carried her cargo in portable tanks, in outward appearance otherwise resembling the typical dry-cargo coaster of that time, with long quarter deck, bridge amidships and engines aft.

Amongst the early diesel and semi-diesel engined craft, a notable group were the five built for the British Petroleum Co. in 1921, and which now form part of the Shell-Mex & B.P. fleet. These were the *Poilo, Perso, Pando, Philo* and *Phero*, most of which were built on the south coast. Each

The s.s. *Tioga*, 742 tons gross. Built at Grangemouth in 1912, and for many years the largest unit in the Anglo-American Oil Co.'s coastal fleet. She had a d.w. capacity of 826 tons and measured 179.9 ft. b.p. by 31.1 ft. beam. Triple-expansion machinery gave her a speed of $9\frac{1}{2}$ knots. Note the towing beam aft.

The m.t. *Tillerman*, 220 tons gross, discharging Regent petrol at Exeter. She was built in 1931 by the N.V. Industrielle Maats. De Noord, Alblasserdam, for C. Rowbotham & Sons, London. Length 114.5 ft., breadth 22.1 ft. 230 tons d.w. One 4-cylinder Deutz engine. Speed 7 knots. Note the awkward trim due to empty forward tanks.

The m.t. *Ben Johnson*, 228 tons gross, a small coastal tanker owned by the National Benzole Co. Ltd. Built 1938 by the Rowhedge Ironworks Co. Ltd., she measures 118 ft. in o.a. length by 22.7 ft. beam. D.w. tonnage 240 on 9ft. $3\frac{1}{2}$ in. draught. One 7-cylinder Polar engine, speed 8 knots.

carried some 500 tons on a draught of 11 ft. 6 in. and was powered by a 180 h.p. four-cylinder Kromhout oil engine and had a 60 h.p. engine of the same type for pumping. These craft, used for supplying oil bunkers to the shipping on the Thames, Mersey, etc., were given a new lease of life in 1951, when they were re-engined with more powerful steam machinery. At the present time Shell-Mex & B.P. Ltd. operate a fleet of well over twenty* harbour, esturial and coastal tankers and have several more on order.

The development of the motor-driven coastal tanker made great strides in the early 'thirties and owed much to Dutch influence: indeed, many of the early ones were built there. One of these was the *Tillerman*, owned by C. Rowbotham & Sons, of London, and built in 1931 by the De Noord yard at Alblasserdam. Designed to serve small ports such as Exeter, etc., she has a deadweight of 230 tons on a draught of only 8 ft. $1\frac{3}{4}$ in. A four-cylinder Deutz engine gives her a speed of 7 knots on a consumption of about one ton of oil per day.

The National Benzole Co. Ltd. has a fleet of rather similar sized ships which are used to distribute their motor spirit. Two are designed for service on the Thames and to pass under the low London bridges: the others for coastal work. Of the latter, the layout of the *Ben Johnson* is typical, although she is their smallest of this type. Built in 1938 by the Rowhedge Ironworks Co. Ltd., she measures 118 ft. in overall length by 22 ft. 6 in. breadth moulded by 10 ft. depth moulded, and is fitted with a seven-cylinder Polar diesel which gives her a service speed of 8 knots. The cargo space, which comprises three sets of tanks (divided by central longitudinal bulkhead), extends from foremast to front of bridge. Abaft this and beneath the bridge is the pumproom, and then the engine room. Forward of the tanks there is a cofferdam and then a deep tank. All accommodation is in the poop, the captain's cabin being on the starboard side forward end. Owing to the low freeboard there are no openings in the poop front, access to the accommodation being by a companion from the deck above.

Besides such small vessels, others of larger tonnage are also used in the coastal and short seas trades. Notable among these are the many war-built

* Excluding very small craft.

The *Britmex No. 4*, 474 tons gross, a dumb oil barge used for port bunkering purposes. One of ten built 1920-1 by Harland & Wolff Ltd. for the British-Mexican Petroleum Co. Ltd. Now owned by the Esso Petroleum Co. Ltd. and employed at Southampton. Length 155 ft., breadth 36.1 ft. 900 tons d.w. on 10 ft. draught. An early photograph, showing *Olympic* (left) and *Aquitania* beyond.

The s.s. *Allurity*, 813 tons gross, owned by F. T. Everard & Sons Ltd. One of the standard *Empire Cadet* type, she was built by A. & J. Inglis Ltd. in 1944, as the *Empire Dombey*. Length o.a. 202.3 ft., breadth 30.7 ft. 850 tons d.w. on 13 ft. 2 in. draught. Triple-expansion machinery. Note the spark arrester on the funnel.

The first British tanker with a Voith-Schneider cycloidal propeller. The m.s. *B. P. Haulier*, built 1955 by James Pollock, Sons & Co. Ltd., Faversham, for Shell-Mex & B.P. Ltd. Designed for esturial service, she has a deadweight of 300 tons on a draught of only 5 ft. 6 in. Length o.a. 140 ft., breadth 27 ft. 6 in. The propeller, which also steers the ship and gives exceptional powers of manoeavrability, consists of a number of blades revolving round a vertical axis.

The *Esso Abingdon*, 446 tons gross, a motor tank barge owned by the Esso Petroleum Co. Ltd. and designed for service on the Thames. She was built in 1952 by Henry Scarr Ltd., Hessle, and measures 168 ft. in length by 32.6 ft. in breadth. The d.w. capacity is 517 tons, on a load draught of 8 ft. 4½ in. A single 4-cylinder Crossley engine gives a speed of 8 knots.

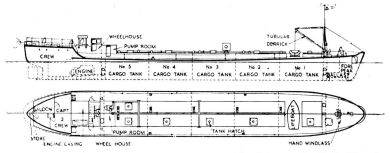

The *Baysdale H.*, a motor lighter of 172 tons gross, owned by John Harker Ltd., Knottingley, Yorks., and used for local river and canal work. Built 1952 by Cook, Welton & Gemmell Ltd., Beverley. Length 138 ft., breadth 17.7 ft. One Gardner engine, speed 9 knots.

The m.s. *Shell Welder*, a coastal tanker of 569 tons gross which was built in 1955 by Clelands (Successors) Ltd., Wallsend-on-Tyne, for Shell-Mex & B.P. Ltd. Intended both for British coasting and Continental voyages, she is of part-welded construction and measures 165 ft. in length b.p. by 29 ft. mld. breadth. A 6-cylinder Crossley engine of 570 b.h.p. gives a service speed of 9¾ knots. She has four pairs of cargo tanks.

standard ships of the *Empire Cadet*, *Ted* and *Tes* types, which feature prominently in the Esso, Shell-Mex & B.P. fleets, and in particular in that of F. T. Everard & Sons Ltd. This family concern, which has its headquarters at the Thameside village of Greenhithe, has a fleet which in recent years has grown enormously in size: one which is by now far the largest of its kind in Britain. The largest units of their tanker fleet—which, unlike most of the others, is run on tramp-ship lines—range from 800 to 3,000 tons gross and are used for carrying both vegetable and mineral oils.

Probably the most important of Britain's inland tankers are the many self-propelled spirit carriers owned by John Harker Ltd., of Knottingly, Yorkshire, which operate on the canals and inland waterways of the Humber and West Yorkshire, etc. The *Baysdale H.*, a typical vessel, built in 1952, measures 138 ft. in length and carries a deadweight of 275 tons on a draught of only 7 ft. She has five tanks with a cofferdam each end of the cargo space and a pumproom that is just forward of the poop. This structure contains all the accommodation, while in the engine room beneath there is a single 152 b.h.p. eight-cylinder Gardner engine which gives her a speed of 9 knots.

The *Australia*, 386 tons gross, a motor tank barge owned by the N.V. Internationale Rivier Tankscheep-vaart Mij., a joint Shell-Van Ommeren concern. The vessel, which has a d.w. tonnage of 773, was built in 1916 as a dumb lighter. She measures 222 ft. × 29 ft. × 5.27 ft. The *Australia*, which is seen passing Bingen, is representative of a large fleet owned by this Company employed in carrying petroleum products to inland depots in Holland and Belgium, and to Basle. Note towing beams aft.

The tank lighter *Regent Linnet*, 104 tons gross, at Stourport, on the River Severn. Owned by the Regent Oil Co. Ltd., she and her sister *Regent Lark* were designed for the inland distribution of Regent petrol. She was built in 1951 by W. J. Yarwood & Sons Ltd., Northwich, and measures 91.5 ft. in overall length and 18.7 ft. in beam. D.w. capacity 130 tons. One 3-cylinder Ruston & Hornsby diesel, speed 7 knots.

Two Esso barges being pushed up river to the Pittsburg plant of the Esso Standard Oil Co. of Pennsylvania. Sizes naturally vary, but a typical tank barge for carrying gasoline and other liquids measures 195 ft. × 35 ft. × 9.5 ft. and has a capacity of 10,000 barrels. Such a craft is suitable for river, lake or short coastwise trips.

Such vessels are dwarfed by the inland tankers used on the Rhine, Danube and other European river and canal systems. The *Australia*, 773 tons deadweight, is representative of a large fleet owned by a joint Shell and Van Ommeren concern, the N.V. Internationale Rivier Tankscheepvaart Mij, used to transport petroleum products from the Shell refinery at Pernis to internal depots in Holland and Belgium, and to the Swiss inland port of Basle. The fleet consists of 41 dumb barges with a total carrying capacity of 52,000 tons, 28 motor barges with a total capacity of 17,000 tons, and two motor tugs. About a dozen dumb barges called *peniches* are used between Strasbourg and Basle, along a specially built canal. This system has been adopted owing to the fact that the Rhine here is so shallow and swift that a percentage of the cargoes of the larger barges has to be transferred to enable them to navigate the upper stretches of this river.

Two types of river tugs—the old and new—at Natchez, on the Mississippi. The stern-wheeler *D. R. Waller* is bound downstream and the twin-screw diesel towboat *William Penn* passes her on her way up-river. Both are towing oil barges.

Tank barges of this type are very long and shallow in relation to their beam and in this the *Australia*'s dimensions, length 222 ft., breadth 29 ft. and depth 5.27 ft., are very typical.

As is well known, the American technique is very different: the popularity of river tugs which push rather than pull groups of square-ended barges which are closely lashed, to form an integrated whole. The Mississippi River system comprises some 10,000 miles of improved navigable waterways: of this about 6,000 miles offers a dependable 9ft. channel, even in dry periods, while on the remainder a 6-ft. channel is provided. After the rains, of course, these figures are infinitely greater. Yet despite this lack of draught a single 'push tow' may have a total lift approaching 20,000 tons. A notable characteristic of many U.S. coastwise tankers is their lack of superstructure, which permits passage under the low bridges

The t.s.s. *Inverlago*, built by Harland & Wolff in 1927 as one of a group of seventeen sisters designed for the Lake Maracaibo service of the Lago Shipping Co. Ltd. She is now owned by the Trinidad Shipping Co. Ltd. Length 305.7 ft., breadth 50.2 ft. D.w. capacity 3,156 tons on 13 ft. 3 in. draught. Triple-expansion engines, speed 8 knots.

The t.s.s. *Rebeca*, a shallow draught tanker of 3,278 tons gross seen discharging at Borburata, Venezuela. One of the Shell fleet, she was built by the Furness S.B. Co. in 1938. Length o.a. 348.2 ft., breadth 56.2 ft. 4,048 tons d.w. Triple-expansion engines, 2,300 i.h.p., speed 11 knots.

The m.s. *Lakeshell*, 2,238 tons gross, owned by Shell Canadian Tankers Ltd. She was designed to deliver petroleum products to the Company's marine terminals on the St. Lawrence River and the Great Lakes, where there is an eight-months' shipping season. Built 1940 by Marine Industries Ltd., at Sorel, P.Q., she measures 259 ft. o.a. × 43.8 ft. D.w. tonnage 2,980. Two 4-cylinder Sulzer diesels, speed 9 knots.

which span the New York State Barge Canal. A typical vessel of this type measures 250 ft. in length, 43 ft. 6 in. in breadth and has six pairs of tanks in which she can carry about 2,500 tons of cargo.

A special type which has been evolved to meet local requirements is the twin-screw shallow-draught tanker, found in numbers in Venezuelan and Caribbean waters. These have relatively great beam, little or no sheer and a raised fo'c'sle and poop, joined by a long trunk deck on which the bridge-house is built. The superstructure aft is almost invariably built out to the hull sides. Beneath, in the engine room, there are two sets of steam reciprocating engines.

The first shallow draught tankers used in this region were a number of former monitors bought by the Shell group from the Royal Navy about 1919, ships which could carry some 440 tons on a draught of about 7 ft. Even so, they had to scrape their way over the bottom as they left their loading jetty and the renewal of keels was anything but unknown. In those early days no dredging was done: instead a channel was worn away by the vessels themselves, one that gradually became deeper and permitted the use of rather larger ships such as the *Francunion* of 1921 (1,320 tons dead-weight on 9 ft. 11 in. draught) and the *President Gomez*, which came from a Dutch yard a year later.

Subsequently many larger craft were built, two notable series being the Shell (Curacaosche) tankers which started with the *Mariquita* and *Juanita* (both of 1923) and of which the *Brigida* was a later example: and the *Inverlago* and her sixteen sisters which were built 1925-28 for the Lago Petroleum Co. by Harland & Wolff Ltd. Taking the *Inverlago* as an example, she is a twin-screw, triple-expansion engined ship measuring 305 ft. (b.p.) by 50 ft. beam, carrying 3,156 tons deadweight on a draught of 13 ft. 3 in. The *Rebeca*, also illustrated, represents a rather larger type built for Shell shortly before the war.

Forerunner of the present Maracaibo tankers. The quad.-screw m.s. *Satoe*, 488 tons gross, one of several small monitors bought by Shell after the first war for conversion into shallow draught tankers. (Dotted lines show former gun position.)

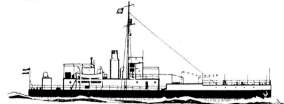

11

Special Types

IN recent years many tankers have been built or modified to carry specialised cargoes such as asphalt and bitumen, molasses, wine and alcohol, chemicals and liquefied gases: others to carry ore one way and oil the other. The pioneer asphalt carrier was the *Arthur W. Sewall,* a steamer of 6,030 tons gross, built in 1926 by Armstrong Whitworth for Norwegians. She was designed to carry very heavy oils, including asphaltic oil from Eastern Venezuela. These for loading and discharge had to be heated to 190 degrees Fahr. and the ship was therefore fitted with a steam coil heating system of far larger capacity than normal. In one tank alone over 4,300 ft. of such piping was fitted. Other early asphalt carriers built 1929-30 were the Palmers-built French-owned *Stanasfalt,* 2,468 tons gross, which had nine cylindrical tanks, and the *Ebano* (2,627 tons gross), a Harland & Wolff product which now trades as the *Esso la Mailleraye.*

An interesting modern example of the asphalt carrier is the *Esso Le Caroubier,* built by a Dutch yard in 1952 for the Esso Standard Co., of Paris. Of 2,730 tons deadweight, she has an overall length of 304 ft., a breadth of 42 ft. and a draught of 16 ft. 1 in. The ship has five cargo tanks which are fitted with heating coils and are designed to limit heat radiation. There is no centreline bulkhead in these, but beneath them is a double bottom, which by covering in the frames, etc., enables the tanks to be cleaned more easily. This feature also serves to raise the centre of gravity. The central asphalt carrying tanks are flanked by wing tanks which are used for ballast. The longitudinal bulkheads either side of the centre tanks slope inwards towards the top (like the sides of the letter A) to reduce, as far as possible, the surface above the cargo which is exposed to the air: also to

The s.s. *Ebano*, an early asphalt carrier built by Harland & Wolff Ltd. in 1929 for the Ebano Oil Co. Ltd. Designed to operate on North Sea service, between Hamburg and Leith. Renamed *Petrophalt* in 1933. Now the *Esso La Mailleraye* of the Esso Standard S.A. Francaise. 2,627 tons gross. Length 290.2 ft., breadth 47.2 ft. One triple-expansion engine.

The m.s. *Esso la Caroubier*, an asphalt carrier of 2,325 tons gross owned by Esso Standard S.A. Francaise. Built in Holland 1952 by Gebr. van der Werf, Deest. D.w. capacity 2,730 tons. One 8 - cylinder Werkspoor diesel, 1,400 b.h.p., speed 11 knots. Note much external similarity with *Bacchus*.

The molasses tanker *Luzon Maru*, 4,120 tons gross, owned by the Nitto Shosen Kabushiki Kaisha. Delivered by the Hiroshima works of the Mitsubishi Shipbuilding & Engineering Co. Ltd., August, 1954. D.w. tonnage 6,249. Length o.a. 373 ft., breadth 53.1 ft. D.R. geared turbine, 2,600 s.h.p., service speed 12½ knots.

give the maximum base area and so allow ample space between the heating coils there, to ease cleaning.

The two eight-inch cargo pump lines are heated by steam pipes, which are attached over their whole length. The two cargo pumps are of rotary type and are driven by shafts reaching from the engine room.

MOLASSES TANKERS

Sugar molasses, which were first carried in any great quantity in the early nineteen-twenties, are far heavier than oil, occupying some $25\frac{1}{2}$ cu. ft. per ton compared with about 40 cu. ft. for oil. It must on no account come into contact with salt water as this results in fermentation and spoiling. Its thickness also calls for an extra elaborate system of heating coils. Owing to its weight this cargo is carried in alternate tanks. The specially designed molasses tanker is usually of the two-deck summer tank type and in size generally ranges between 10,000 and 15,000 tons deadweight.

WINE CARRIERS

It is said in Holland that Russia was the first to use a tanker for carrying wine. Shortly after the first world war a Russian ship came to the west with a cargo of Crimean wine, for which bids were invited. So poor in quality that it hardly deserved its name, the wine, it is said, was sold for only a penny a gallon. Most important of the advantages of carrying wine in bulk is the very great economy in space as compared with the traditional use of casks, also the far quicker turn-round which is made possible.

About 1935 a French company, Soflumar, of Paris (a subsidiary of the Dutch firm of Van Ommeren), converted a cargo ship to carry wine in bulk. This was the appropriately named *Bacchus*, 2,500 tons deadweight, whose two holds were divided into forty tanks. They had a capacity of 337,000 gallons and were lined with a substance named brauthite, which was impervious to the action of wine. After unloading, the tanks could be cleaned by means of an ingenious system whereby any lees could be removed. Thus a degree of purity was obtained which the owners said was impossible with casks. The ship was employed between Algiers and Rouen and carried as many as thirty different varieties at a time. Subsequently sunk during the war, she has been replaced by a new *Bacchus*, which is the most important of her type afloat.

The m.s. *Bacchus*, 3,256 tons gross, a wine tanker owned by 'Soflumar,' Paris. Completed by the Rotterdam Dry Dock Co. in July, 1949. Length o.a. 334 ft., breadth 47.2 ft. 3,980 tons d.w. on 19 ft. 4 in. draught. One 3-cylinder Doxford type engine, speed 12½ knots. Has forty wine tanks.

Built in Holland in 1949, she has a gross tonnage of 3,256 and outwardly resembles a normal motor tanker. She carries 3,980 tons deadweight and has 40 tanks for wine or alcohol. Electric pumps and copper conduit pipes treated with a special varnish are used for loading and discharge. Under and beside the main wine tanks are others which are partly used for water ballast. At the bottom of the ship a tunnel running the length of the tanks contains all the conduits and stop-cocks for the cargo, so that no conduits pass through the tanks. In the pumproom the *Bacchus* has two electrically-driven cargo pumps, each with a capacity of 80 tons per hour, as well as two 140-ton ballast pumps. Her main propelling motor consists of a three-cylinder Doxford type engine of 2,100 h.p. Besides this ship and the specially designed *Sahel* and *Mitidja*, many small coasters and converted cargo ships have appeared in this trade, including for a while several of the British war-built *Empire Cadet* class.

LIQUID GAS CARRIERS

Although the transport of liquid petroleum gas in tankers goes back to pre-war days and several ships have been converted for this purpose, the increasing use of butane gas has led to the appearance of several specially designed craft in European waters. The first of these was the *Rasmus Tholstrop*, 499 tons gross, built at Marstrand in 1953, for the A/S Kosangas, of Copenhagen, and which carried 320 tons of liquid gas in twelve upright cylindrical tanks. She was joined a year later by the *Sorine Tholstrop* (148 tons gross), for an associated firm, and which had a single 90-ton tank.

The autumn of 1954 saw the completion of the *Cap Carbon* (905 tons gross), which had been built by the Foxhol shipyard and fitted out by the Amsterdam Dry Dock Co. for the Soc. Anon. de Gerance et d'Armement, of Paris. Her hull is of typical coaster design and has an overall length of 209 ft., a breadth of 33 ft. and a depth of 14 ft. 9 in. On a draught of 13 ft. 2 in., she is designed to carry 435 tons of liquid gas in fourteen vertical cylindrical tanks, these being arranged in two rows between the fo'c'sle and poop. The cargo is handled by two compressors, each with a capacity of 100 cubic metres of liquid per hour, and a pump of the same capacity.

There is an elaborate fire-fighting installation, consisting of a battery of 37 CO_2 cylinders, which serve the cargo spaces as well as the pump and motor room forward. Each compartment has a self-contained installation, which is remote controlled from the bridge. The propelling motor of this interesting ship, which is designed for service between Marseilles and North Africa, consists of a supercharged eight-cylinder direct-reversible Deutz engine. This develops 1,000 b.h.p. at 380 b.h.p. and gives a loaded service speed of 10 knots.

In the United States several much larger vessels have been converted to carry petroleum gas, notably the *Natalie D. Warren* (7,298 tons gross), a former C1-A type turbine-driven ship, which in 1947 was reconstructed by the Bethlehem Steel Co. for the Warren Petroleum Corporation. In her five holds no less than 68 tall cylindrical tanks were fitted. These rested on the tank tops, their crowns projecting some twelve feet above the weather deck. She was followed by the rather smaller *Ultragaz*, a dry-cargo ship of 2,490 tons gross, which was similarly given 31 cylinders.

CHEMICAL TANKERS

Others, including several oil tankers, were altered to carry chemicals in bulk. Most important of these were the *Marine Chemist* (8,137 tons gross), formerly the *W. H. Ferguson*, and the *R. E. Wilson* (9,987 tons gross), ex *Monocacy*, which were fitted to carry chemicals in centre compartments and petroleum in the wing tanks.

The first tanker, however, to be specially designed to carry chemicals

The *Cap Carbon*, a butane gas carrying motor tanker of 1,075 tons d.w. Built 1954 by the N.V. Scheepswerf 'Foxhol' v/h Gebr. Muller for the Soc. Anon. de Gerance et d'Armement (S.A.G.A.), Paris, she has an overall length of 209 ft. and carries her cargo (435 tons) in fourteen portable tanks. She is designed for Marseilles-North Africa service and is fitted with a 1,000 b.h.p. Deutz engine which gives a speed of 10 knots.

Left: View from bridge, looking forward over the tank tops.

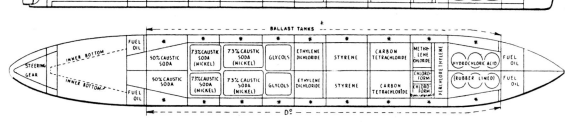

	BALLAST TANKS											
FUEL OIL	50% CAUSTIC SODA	73% CAUSTIC SODA (NICKEL)	73% CAUSTIC SODA (NICKEL)	GLYCOLS	ETHYLENE DICHLORIDE	STYRENE	CARBON TETRACHLORIDE	METHYLENE CHLORIDE	PERCHLORETHYLENE	HYDROCHLORIC ACID	FUEL OIL
FUEL OIL	50% CAUSTIC SODA	73% CAUSTIC SODA (NICKEL)	73% CAUSTIC SODA (NICKEL)	GLYCOLS	ETHYLENE DICHLORIDE	STYRENE	CARBON TETRACHLORIDE	CHLORO-FORM / KHLORO FORM	PERCHLORETHYLENE	(RUBBER LINED)	FUEL OIL

STEERING GEAR — INNER BOTTOM — INNER BOTTOM

The s.s *Marine Dow-Chem*, 9,936 tons gross, owned by the Marine Chemical Transport Co. Inc. The first large ship to be specially built to carry liquid chemicals. These call for special protection, both against contamination and corrosion. Built and engined 1954 by Bethlehem, Quincy. Length o.a. 551 ft., breadth mld. 68 ft. Capacity (chemicals) 3½ million gallons. D.R. geared turbines, 7,700 s.h.p., speed 15 knots.

in bulk was the *Marine Dow-Chem*, a twin-screw turbine-driven vessel of 9,936 tons gross. She was built in 1954 by the Bethlehem Shipbuilding Co., Quincy, Mass., for the Marine Chemical Transport Co. Inc. Chartered to the Dow Chemical Co., she is used to carry cargoes from that company's Texas plant to various U.S. ports and others in the Caribbean, Central and South America.

Externally she appears to be of orthodox oil tanker design, but apart from the machinery space her internal arrangements differ in many ways, the most important being the protective arrangements for the cargo tanks.

Chemicals must always be protected from contamination, for quality in that industry is computed on a 'parts per million' basis. Besides the problem of ensuring strict quality control in the tanks, there was the fact that she was required to carry mixed cargoes of up to eleven different products, each with its individual characteristics. An additional requirement was that sea water must not come into contact with loaded tanks. To provide isolation for each part of the cargo the ship was given double bulkheads, which ensured a minimum of two thicknesses of steel between any two cargo tanks and cargo tank and sea.

Tanks for the various types of cargo are each fitted with separate transfer systems, pipes, pumps, connections, etc., so the vessel can load or discharge all sections of a mixed cargo simultaneously. The loss of deadweight and cubic capacity brought about by this elaborate subdivision results in the ship having a cargo volume some 54 per cent. of that of an oil tanker of the same dimensions and displacement.

ORE AND OIL CARRIERS

The combined ore and oil carrier is almost invariably a vessel of considerable size. The type first made its appearance in 1921 when the Bethlehem Sparrows Point yard built the *G. Harrison Smith*, a ship of 14,305 tons gross, for Canadian owners. She was designed to carry oil to South America in side tanks, and return with ore, in centre compartments. A twin-screw ship, she was fitted with triple expansion engines of 4,100 i.h.p., which gave her a speed of $10\frac{1}{2}$ knots. Later this remarkable vessel became the *Charles G. Black* of the Standard Oil Company, of New Jersey, a firm who kept her for seventeen years. The ore compartments were retained, but even without them she had a cargo capacity of 140,050 barrels. The only one of her type in the Esso fleet, she was sold to the Ore S.S. Corporation in 1940, and as their *Venore* operated until 1942, when she was torpedoed.

The most notable of European ore-carrying fleets is that of the Grangesberg-Oxelosund Co., of Stockholm. Starting with the *Rautus* of 1944, this Swedish mining company built a series of combined ore/oil carriers. She and her sister *Raunala* were 12-knot motor ships of 12,100 tons deadweight, but the next two, the *Porjus* and *Pajala* of 1950-51 were rather larger, 13-knotters with a deadweight capacity of 15,600 tons. After gaining experience with these the company ordered a series of far larger vessels, the Gotaverken-built *Tarfala*, 14 knots, 26,000 tons deadweight, and three of rather smaller size, the *Vittangi*, *Vasara* and *Vistasvagge*. The last named, which is the newest, was delivered by Kockums Mek. Verksted, of Malmo, on March 10th, 1955, is strengthened for navigation in ice and designed to carry a full cargo of either ore or oil, or, under special conditions, a cargo of both kinds at the same time. Ore is loaded in two large holds in the centre of the ship, while oil is carried in 22 side tanks. The hull is longitudinally framed and every side tank has three web frames. The transverse bulkheads in the oil tanks are corrugated, while the two longitudinal ones are stiffened with the smooth sides turned towards the ore hold.

The m.s. *Vistasvagge*, 16,207 tons gross, a combined ore and tank vessel owned by the Trafikaktiebolaget Grangesberg-Oxelosund, of Stockholm. Built in 1955 by Kockums M.V., Malmo, she has a deadweight of 21,400 tons and is designed to carry a full load of either ore or oil, the volume of the ore holds being 378,450 cu. ft. and that of the oil tanks 781,160 cu. ft. She and *Soya Atlantic* (*opposite*) have similar hulls but differ in machinery, midship boat fittings and foremast.

The s.s. *Soya Atlantic*, 16,485 tons gross, an ore/oil carrier, built 1954 by Kockums M.V. for the Rederi A/B Walltank (O. Wallenius), of Stockholm. The first large turbine driven ship to be built and owned in Sweden, she is propelled by a De Laval turbine and two Foster Wheeler boilers, which give a loaded speed of 15 knots. The two central ore holds are specially shaped for easy grab discharge, while under and at the sides of these are twenty-two L-shaped oil cargo tanks. Her d.w. tonnage is 21,770. Note small oil hatches at sides, corrugated covers to centreline ones. Also the rounded sheer strake, which is of special high-tensile steel.

The *Vistasvagge* has an overall length of 595 ft. 9½ in., a moulded breadth of 74 ft. 6 in., and a moulded depth of 44 ft. 3in. The deadweight capacity is 21,400 tons on a draught of 31 ft. The eleven cargo hatches for the ore holds are hydraulically operated, being opened and closed in pairs by hydraulic power from a pump station in the bridge. In twelve minutes all hatches can be opened, while their closing takes but three to four minutes. Should the hydraulic system be temporarily out of use, the hatches can be operated by the ship's winches. The propelling machinery consists of an eight-cylinder Kockums-M.A.N. diesel developing 8,450 b.h.p. and giving a loaded speed of 14¾ knots. The bridgehouse, though tall, is very short and only contains the captain's sea cabin and another cabin for the pilot. The rest of the accommodation is aft, where each of the crew has a single-berth cabin.

Another important group of combined ore and oil carriers is that of the *Bomi Hills* class, built in 1952 by the Fairfield Co. Ltd., for the Skibs A/S Orenor, of Oslo. Single-screw motor ships of 22,250 tons deadweight, they are of generally similar hold/tank layout, except that they have deep tanks forward for the carriage of latex. As the tanker's traditional fore and aft gangway would have obstructed cargo handling, this feature was eliminated. Instead, along the top of the inner sides of the longitudinal bulkheads there are two fore and aft passageways, one for the use of personnel and the other to take the pipelines usually found on the fore and aft gangway.

NAVAL TANKERS

The naval tanker is another highly specialised type. Not only is she required to carry considerable quantities of oil—probably of several grades, but if she is used for fleet replenishment work she will need a large amount of store and provision space. The work of refuelling at sea calls for good manoeuvrability and also the provision of special deck and derrick equipment. One of the most interesting examples of this type is the Peruvian naval tanker *Sechura*, which was delivered by John I. Thornycroft & Co. Ltd. early in 1955. A ship of 6,000 tons deadweight, she has an overall length of 385 ft., a moulded breadth of 52 ft. and a moulded depth of 26 ft. Her equipment is such that she can refuel two ships at sea simultaneously— one a side—while under way. She has 22 cargo oil tanks, divided longitudinally by two corrugated bulkheads. Besides these there is a dry-cargo hold forward, fitted with a MacGregor patent hatch cover. The foremast, which is adjacent, carries two 7-ton and one 12-ton derricks. A five-cylinder B. & W. type diesel engine of 2,400 b.h.p. gave her a loaded trial speed of $13\frac{1}{4}$ knots.

The Peruvian Naval tanker *Sechura*, 6,000 tons d.w. Built 1955 by John I. Thornycroft & Co. Ltd., Southampton. Length o.a. 385 ft., breadth mld. 52 ft. Displacement tonnage 8,700. One 5-cylinder B. & W. type diesel engine, 2,400 b.h.p., speed on trial 13¼ knots. Note the Thornycroft type top to the funnel, an innovation among tankers.

The R.F.A. *Wave Laird*, 8,187 tons gross, refuelling H.M.S. *Theseus* in Korean waters. Originally the *Empire Dunbar*, one of the 15-knot standard tankers, she was built in 1946 by Sir James Laing & Sons Ltd. Length o.a. 494 ft., breadth 64 ft. 11,600 tons d.w. Single screw, double reduction geared turbines, 6,800 s.h.p. One of twenty similar ships, all of which have *Wave* names.

The *Tide Austral*, 13,165 tons gross, built 1955 for the Royal Australian Navy by Harland & Wolff Ltd. Designed as a fast fleet replenishment tanker, she has a deadweight of 17,700 tons, an o.a. length of 583 ft. and a breadth of 71 ft. A single-screw ship, she is powered by Pametrada geared turbines and three Babcock boilers. Three sisters, *Tiderace*, *Tiderange* and *Tidereach*, were built for the Royal Navy by Thompson, Laing, and Swan Hunter. Note the elaborate gear amidships for refuelling at sea.

The s.s. *Esso Annapolis*, 11,316 tons gross. Built in 1940 by the Bethlehem Steel Co., Sparrows Point, for the Standard Oil Co., of New Jersey, she was the first of a group of twenty-four from these builders which incorporated special defence features, notably extra powerful turbine machinery and hull lines (including a bulbous bow) which gave them a speed of 18 knots. The successful operation of these ships had an important influence in raising the speeds of subsequent large commercial tanker designs. The *Esso Annapolis*, which has operated for most of her life as the U.S. Naval oiler *Chemung*, has an overall length of 553 ft., a breadth mld. of 75 ft. and twin-screw geared turbines of 15,200 b.h.p.

The Royal Fleet Auxiliary tanker *Olna*, 12,695 tons gross, with gear ready for refuelling at sea. One of two ordered by Shell from Swan, Hunter, & Wigham Richardson Ltd., she was taken over by the Admiralty while building. Her sister *Hyalina* is still in the Shell fleet. Length o.a. 583 ft., breadth 70 ft., d.w. tonnage 17,500. Single-screw B.T.H. turbo-electric machinery and three Babcock & Wilcox boilers, 13,000 s.h.p. Speed 17 knots.

The fleet tanker *Eddycreek*, 2,224 tons gross. Built for the Admiralty in 1953 by Lobnitz & Co. Ltd., she is one of a group of eight constructed at various shipyards. Length o.a. 286 ft., breadth 44 ft. 2,095 tons d.w. on 17 ft. 2 in. draught. One enclosed triple-expansion engine by builders, 1,700 i.h.p., speed 12 knots. The base of the bridge section contains large store rooms.

12

Super Tankers

AS a result of the ever increasing demand for oil the post-war construction of tankers has reached hitherto undreamed-of levels, while in relation to the rest of the world's merchant tonnage the tanker has never before held such an important position, either numerically or as regards size and performance.

In the days before the first world war the Eagle Oil Transport Co. set an early lead by ordering a group of ten ships of 15,000-16,000 tons deadweight, capping these at the end of the war with a further six, turbine-driven craft each with a deadweight capacity of 18,000 tons. But apart from such isolated examples as the 17,000-ton *Cadillac* and *Saranac*, which were built in 1917-18 for the Anglo-American Oil Co., and a few others—mostly U.S.-built—owners showed little desire for such outsize vessels.

Instead, during the 'twenties the most general size was around 10,000-11,000 tons deadweight, figures which by the late 'thirties had slowly risen to 15,000-16,000 tons. Even then, however, the 12,000-tonner, drawing 27 to 28 ft. of water, was regarded as the best general purpose ship. The service speeds of these vessels was seldom much over 11 knots. New standards, however, were set by the vast numbers of T2 type tankers built in the United States during the second world war. Ships of over 16,000 tons deadweight, they were capable of 14-14½ knots and had remarkably efficient cargo pumping equipment. A small but outstanding group built in Great Britain comprised the three *Helicina* class ships, which had turbo-electric machinery and a trial speed of 17 knots. The first of these was completed in 1945 as the *Olna*, having been taken over by the Admiralty while under construction. These three were, however, designed to meet

The s.s. *Saranac*, 12,074 tons gross, built 1918 by Palmers, Newcastle, for the Anglo-American Oil Co. Later she and her sister *Cadillac* were given new centre sections. Sunk by U-boat in the Atlantic, June, 1940. 16,870 tons d.w. Length 530.5 ft., breadth 66.3 ft. Single-screw quad.-expansion engines and four Scotch boilers, 220 lb. pressure. Speed 10½ knots.

special war-time needs, and other tankers built then and immediately after the war were of more modest size and power.

During the late 'forties a number of tankers of over 20,000 tons deadweight were ordered, including a series of over a dozen 24,000-tonners which were designed and built by the Furness S.B. Co. Ltd., mostly for Norwegian or other independent owners. The first of this group, the *C. J. Hambro*, was completed in 1949 and marked the beginning of a new phase in large tanker construction.

The *Velutina* (28,000 tons deadweight), the first of four sisters for Shell, entered service a year later and for a while she held the record for size among British owned tankers. Now ships of over 30,000 tons deadweight are found in both the Shell and British Tanker Co.'s fleets, while others of up to 38,000 and 42,000 tons deadweight respectively are on order. Few of these, however, are due for early delivery. At the end of 1955 they were the largest yet ordered by British concerns, although several independent firms had bigger vessels already in service. Amongst these were the *Tina Onassis* (45,750 tons deadweight) and the *Al-Malik Saud Al-Awal* (47,000 tons), built in Germany for the Onassis group, the Japanese built *Phoenix* (44,633 tons deadweight) and the American built *World Glory* (45,509 tons), both of which entered service in 1954.

Amongst new construction at that date the 47,750-ton *Spyros Niarchos*, the first of a pair for the Niarchos group, was fitting out; a ship which was not only the largest afloat to be solely designed for oil carrying but also the largest merchant ship of any type to be built in Great Britain since the war. Notable amongst others on order were some for the Tidewater Associated

The s.s. *Velutina*, 18,666 tons gross. The first of the super-tankers to be built for the Shell fleet, she was launched by Princess Margaret in April, 1950. Length o.a. 643 ft., breadth 81 ft., d.w. tonnage 28,330. Single-screw geared turbines, speed 16 knots. Builders: Swan, Hunter, & Wigham Richardson Ltd. Followed by sisters *Verena*, *Volsella* and *Velletia*.

The s.s. *Tina Onassis*, 25,010 tons gross, built 1953 by Howaldtswerke, Hamburg, for the Palmas Transportation Co., Monrovia, one of the Onassis group of companies. She has an overall length of 775 ft. and a breadth of 95 ft. Her d.w. capacity is 45,750 tons on 37 ft. 6 in. draught. D.R. geared turbines of 17,000 s.h.p. give her a service speed of 16½ knots. She has twenty-nine oil tanks and five oil pumps with a total capacity of 5,000 tons per hour. There is accommodation for eight passengers.

The s.s. *Phoenix*, 25,733 tons gross. Built 1954 for Universal Tankships Inc., of Monrovia and New York, a subsidiary of National Bulk Carriers. Built in Japan by the parent company's Kure Shipyard Division. Like most others in this fleet, she has the minimum of superstructure. Length 680 ft., breadth 97 ft. D.R. geared turbines, speed about 16 knots.

Oil Co., of San Francisco, of which two from a French yard will carry 51,850 tons deadweight. The largest yet contracted for are three for the Ludwig group, from their Kure shipyard in Japan. One of these, an oil and ore carrier, will be of 58,000 tons deadweight and the other two 'pure' oil tankers of over 82,000 tons apiece.

Not only does the Ludwig group of companies have the biggest of tankers on order, but in December, 1955, one of their ships carried the largest oil cargo yet, one of 51,330 tons, from Mena al Ahmadi on the Persian Gulf to Santos. Like others in this fleet the ship, the *Sinclair Petrolore*, is not solely designed for oil carrying, but is a combined oil/ore carrier and is described by her classification society as a 'self-unloading bulk carrier or oil tanker.' Then on her maiden voyage, the *Sinclair Petrolore* was drawing about two feet short of her maximum draught, which is 40 ft. $6\frac{1}{2}$ in. Delivered by the Kure Shipyard in October, the vessel is owned by Universe Tankships, Inc., New York, has a maximum deadweight capacity of 55,000 tons and measures 756 ft. in length b.p. and 106 ft. in breadth. It will be seen that when referring to size records a subtle distinction has to be drawn between vessels solely designed for oil carrying and the combined oil/ore ships.

It is not size alone which has earned these large ships the title of 'Super' tanker, but also their speed and general performance, which in most cases are generally greatly superior to those of the average-sized vessels. Two main factors have encouraged the building of these great ships; one, the United States policy of conserving her resources of crude oil, and the other, the switch-over from refining at source to refining near the area of consumption. The new refineries which have been recently built in many parts of the world have facilities for the reception of the large ships which can most conveniently supply the vast quantities of crude oil they need. In others trades the giant tanker is handicapped by the inability to enter many smaller ports. Another problem is that in the event of an accident, there is the possibility of having to go a great distance before reaching a dry dock large enough to accommodate her. Although it is mainly draught which limits the trading flexibility of the large tanker, the length and breadth also offer restrictions in some ports. For instance, the greatest permissible length for tankers navigating the River Seine is 557 ft.

On two of the main hauls, namely the Persian Gulf to the United Kingdom/Continent and the United States, a draught limit is imposed by

The s.s. *World Glory*, 27,812 tons gross. Built 1954 for the World Tanker Corporation, Monrovia, by the Bethlehem Steel Co., Shipbuilding Division, Quincy, Mass. Length o.a. 736 ft., breadth 102 ft. D.w. capacity 45,509 tons on 37 ft. 6 in. draught. Eleven triple tanks. Discharge capacity 4,000 tons per hour. D.R. geared turbines, steam 600 lb., 850 deg. F. Speed on load trials 17.44 knots.

the Suez Canal and at the present time the largest tankers making transit are unable to load to full capacity. Eventually, when the current dredging programme is completed vessels drawing up to 36 ft. will be able to pass through the canal. Another stage towards this goal was reached in March, 1955, when ships drawing up to 35 ft. were allowed to make experimental transits. The importance of the Suez Canal to tanker owners may be gauged by the figures for November, 1955, when north-bound oil shipments through the canal totalled 5,123,209 tons, of which 4,604,421 tons were of crude oil.

Despite these and other restrictions, the use of large tankers brings considerable operating economy. In this respect it has been calculated that the cost of transporting a ton of oil from Curacao to the United Kingdom in a ship of 30,000 tons is little more than half the cost in the case of a 10,000-ton vessel of equal speed. Here it must be remembered that as ships increase in size, so higher speeds become permissible. Whereas the economical average speed for a tanker of 10,000 tons deadweight is around $11\frac{1}{2}$ knots, that of the 20,000-tonner is $13\frac{1}{2}$ knots. Similarly, the most economical speed for a ship of 30,000 tons deadweight is around 15 knots. Above or below those speeds she will not be operating as efficiently as she should.

As regards propelling machinery, almost all tankers of over 24,000 tons deadweight are turbine-driven, although notable exceptions are the Norwegian-owned *Ferncrest* (34,500 tons deadweight), which when launched in 1955 was the world's largest motor tanker, the three *Berge* ships and the 31,370-ton *Octavian*. As they descend from the 24,000 mark an ever increasing majority are fitted with diesels, although American owners invariably prefer turbines, as has the Shell group for their fifty 18,000-ton general purpose ships. In the not too distant future it seems likely that yet another form of propulsion—that of the gas turbine—will become widely used.

Both structurally and as regards internal layout the super-tanker does not differ very materially from the smaller vessel. The increase in size, however, has shown in several recent instances of fracture that these large vessels are subjected to greater stress and strain than was first realised, and Lloyd's Register of Shipping have amended the Society's Construction

Rules for welded ships. These prescribe more specific requirements of the design and extend the use of specially approved notch-tough steels for important points of the main structure.

In closing it may be appropriate to give some particulars of one of these super-tankers, the *World Glory*, which was built in 1954 by the Bethlehem Steel Corporation, Shipbuilding Division, at Quincy, Mass., for one of the Niarchos group of companies, the World Tankers Co. Inc. As shown in the illustration on page 139, she is of the usual three-island type, with two pairs of kingposts and a single thick-rooted mast that is stepped on the bridgehouse. The hull, which contains 33 separate cargo tanks, each 40 ft. long, has an overall length of 736 ft. The moulded breadth is 102 ft. and the moulded depth 50 ft. The deadweight capacity when loaded to her summer draught of 37 ft. 6 in. is 45,509 long tons. The displacement at this figure is 58,265 long tons.

The *World Glory* is fitted with a single five-bladed manganese bronze propeller—one of the largest ever cast—and is powered by D.R. geared turbines designed to deliver 15,000 s.h.p. at 100 propeller revolutions per minute. On trials in August, 1954, she averaged 17.1 knots at this power, when ballasted to her service draught with water, although her designed service speed is 16 knots. Her unusually high ratio of speed to horse-power and tonnage is largely due to the builders' 'Clearwater' type stern and advanced hull form. This form of stern, found on the fast *Mariner* type ships, but not previously on a tanker, allows greater clearance fore and aft of the propeller and permits the latter to be located deeper in the water.

The *World Glory* has a liquid cargo capacity of 16,614,696 gallons (395,588 barrels) and to handle this she has two turbine-driven and two centrifugal pumps together capable of handling 1,000,000 gallons of oil per hour. There are four separate piping systems, enabling her to carry four different grades of oil, and load or discharge these simultaneously without fear of contamination.

Although not quite the largest of tankers, the *World Glory* has a length that is exceeded by only five passenger liners, the two *Queens*, the *United States* and the French Line's *Liberte* and *Ile De France*. The internal layout of the newer and larger *Spyros Niarchos* is shown on pages 14 and 15.

13

Some Leading Tanker Fleets

VARIOUS of the world's more interesting or important tanker fleets feature on the following pages. Tanker owning firms are so numerous that it is obviously impossible to show more than a representative few, and this is particularly true of American concerns.

To delve fully into the spheres of operation and ownership would alone call for a large book, not a few pages. For example, the tankers themselves may be operated by the oil producing companies, or by subsidiary companies, or by a jointly held subsidiary company, by direct charter, or by the subsidizing of an independent company or firm by long term charter. The variety of flags under which the ships operate are legion and the vessels of one large oil concern may fly the colours of a dozen different nations.

The following figures for the world tanker fleet are kindly supplied by Messrs. John I. Jacobs & Co. Ltd.

World Tanker Fleet

2,000 tons d.w. and over as at 31st December, 1955

FLAG	MOTOR		STEAM		TOTAL	
	No.	Deadweight	No.	Deadweight	No.	Deadweight
U.S.	57	322,092	463	7,807,943	520	8,130,035
British	337	4,318,838	200	3,160,441	537	7,479,279
Norwegian ..	370	5,929,176	29	366,196	399	6,295,372
Liberian	34	512,526	151	3,592,072	185	4,104,598
Panamanian ..	51	788,578	133	2,380,465	184	3,169,043
French	66	984,750	48	896,788	114	1,881,538
Italian	68	900,724	51	869,743	119	1,770,467

WORLD TANKER FLEET

FLAG	MOTOR		STEAM		TOTAL	
	No.	Deadweight	No.	Deadweight	No.	Deadweight
Dutch	64	662,260	51	714,187	115	1,376,447
Swedish	74	1,193,614	3	46,920	77	1,240,534
Japanese	21	370,434	36	574,282	57	944,716
Danish	47	789,293	—	—	47	789,293
Argentine.. ..	21	198,956	25	236,351	46	435,307
German	28	310,776	5	102,845	33	413,621
Russian	37	325,659	6	35,657	43	361,316
Spanish	25	237,202	7	50,177	32	287,379
Canadian	18	57,048	28	226,734	46	283,782
Greek	1	17,610	17	237,012	18	254,622
Honduran ..	4	59,884	7	166,665	11	226,549
Brazilian	12	202,770	2	21,030	14	223,800
Venezuelan ..	7	42,680	25	166,368	32	209,048
Finnish	13	185,565	1	11,350	14	196,915
Mexican	9	84,384	11	109,692	20	194,076
Belgian	7	86,684	3	82,825	10	169,509
Portuguese ..	8	110,607	1	2,525	9	113,132
Turkish	4	34,713	4	45,598	8	80,311
Saudi-Arabian ..	—	—	1	46,550	1	46,550
Chinese	2	24,628	1	11,900	3	36,528
Uruguayan ..	—	—	2	33,230	2	33,230
Polish	1	9,481	2	20,292	3	29,773
Chilean	—	—	3	26,447	3	26,447
Egyptian	1	16,900	1	8,500	2	25,400
South African ..	1	24,600	—	—	1	24,600
Peruvian	2	10,800	3	12,986	5	23,786
Costa Rican ..	1	10,509	1	12,012	2	22,521
Israeli	—	—	2	21,823	2	21,823
Yugoslav	2	21,710	—	—	2	21,710
Australian ..	—	—	1	17,700	1	17,700
Korean	2	5,640	2	11,148	4	16,788
Moroccan.. ..	2	15,137	—	—	2	15,137
Siamese	1	2,000	2	9,159	3	11,159
Pakistan	—	—	1	9,760	1	9,760
Colombian ..	1	4,315	1	3,065	2	7,380
Irish	—	—	1	3,350	1	3,350
New Zealand ..	1	3,325	—	—	1	3,325
Dominican ..	—	—	1	3,156	1	3,156
	1,400	18,875,868	1,332	22,154,944	2,732	41,030,812

The m.s. *Athelmere*, 7,254 tons gross, built 1954 by Hawthorn Leslie (Shipbuilders) Ltd. Length o.a. 459 ft., breadth 61 ft. One Hawthorn-Doxford engine gives a speed of 13 knots. A notable feature of her design is the ability to carry chemicals, to the extent of some 2,000 tons.

The m.s. *Athelbeach*, 7,533 tons gross, built 1950 by Hawthorn Leslie (Shipbuilders) Ltd., for the Athel Line Ltd. She has a d.w. tonnage of 10,390 on a draught of 25 ft. 6 in., measures 459 ft. in overall length and 61 ft. in breadth. One 4-cylinder Doxford type engine gives a speed of 13 knots.

The s.s. *Athelbrook*, 808 tons gross, built 1950 by Cammell Laird & Co. Ltd. for Athel Line Ltd. Designed for local service in the West Indies, she has four pairs of cargo tanks, and a d.w. capacity of 743 tons on a draught of 11 ft. 11 in. The overall length is 183 ft. and the breadth 32 ft. Single-screw triple-expansion machinery of 500 i.h.p. and one boiler give a speed of 8¾ knots.

Athel Line

The Athel Line tankers are designed for carrying molasses, a cargo far heavier than oil, occupying $25\frac{1}{2}$ cu. ft. to the ton, compared with $39\frac{1}{2}$-40 cu. ft. for heavy oils. Although similar in outward appearance the internal arrangements of molasses tankers are unlike those of other modern tankers for they are of summer tank design and have only one longitudinal bulkhead. To reduce bending movement and ensure the best distribution of weight the cargo is carried in alternate tanks, the length of these being limited to 30 ft.

The molasses trade is a seasonal one and as storage facilities in the West Indies are limited prompt collection is necessary. Therefore, vessels of relatively modest size are preferable to fewer, larger ones. Cargo is collected from many different points in the West Indies area, there being about thirty in Cuba alone, four in S. Domingo and about six in Puerto Rico. Besides these there are a great many more in the British West Indies, where two coasters are used to collect supplies from the scattered mills. The bulk of this, known as blackstrap, is brought to the U.K./Continent for animal feeding. Molasses are also used by distillers who, however, prefer the invert variety, which has a higher sugar content.

The Athel ships normally take cargo one way only, but the *Athelmere* built in 1954 was designed to carry up to 2,000 tons of liquid chemicals, while the *Athelstane*, delivered in August, 1955, can not only carry molasses, oil or spirit in bulk, but also a full cargo of liquid chemicals such as aqua ammonia and caustic soda liquor. Excluding several coasters, the Athel fleet totals fifteen ocean-going units belonging to three main size groups; vessels of about 10,400 tons deadweight, which have a draught of 25 ft. 6 in., those of 13,200 tons deadweight and 28 ft. 2 in. draught and the large units, which do much time charter work and have a deadweight capacity of 15,600 tons on 28 ft. 9 in. Besides these there is one motor tanker of 10,000 tons deadweight on order.

British Tanker Company

At the close of 1955 the fleet owned by the British Tanker Company totalled just under 150 ships, while the Company also had a further thirty-two either under construction or on order. A breakdown into size groups is both interesting and revealing and shows that of those in service there were twelve super-tankers, six of 32,000 tons deadweight and six of 28,000 tons. Of 16,000-tonners there were twenty new vessels and several of the American T2 design. The long popular 12,000-ton type numbered over eighty: incidentally, three of these, the appropriately named *British Escort*, *British Pilot* and *British Swordfish* were originally M.A.C. ships. Of the earlier 10,000-ton type, which once formed the backbone of the fleet, only three, the *British Faith, British Hope* and *British Prestige* remained. Next there were thirteen, each of 8,000 tons deadweight, built 1943-51. Finally, three home trade and coastal ships, the *British Bugler* and *British Drummer* of 5,000 tons deadweight and the *British Scout*, 2,200 tons.

Of those on order almost all will be of very large size. The programme is headed by four of 42,000 tons deadweight, while there will also be fourteen of 34,500 tons (eight from British and six from Italian yards) as well as eight 32,000-tonners. Lower down the scale are two 18,000-ton general purpose tankers, which, unlike the rest, will be diesel driven.

Originally the Company's funnel design consisted of a black stack, with white disc and band on a broader red band, the disc bearing the black painted letters B.T.C. Later, in the 'twenties this was changed to the familiar red, black topped funnel, which bore one green and two white bands. In 1954 it was decided to superimpose on these the well-known B.P. shield, green with yellow letters. In October of that year the *British Soldier* became the first ship to carry this new marking.

28,000-ton d.w. type *British Adventure*, length o.a. 643 ft.

The m.s. *British Sergeant*, 10,073 tons gross. Built and engined 1954 by Harland & Wolff Ltd., Glasgow. Length o.a. 516 ft., breadth 66 ft. Nine triple tanks. D.w. capacity 16,000 tons. One 6-cylinder Harland-B. & W. type diesel engine, 4,500 b.h.p., speed 12 knots. One of a numerous class—the largest diesel driven units in the British Tanker fleet.

The m.s. *British Diligence*, 8,408 tons gross, built 1937 by Swan, Hunter, & Wigham Richardson Ltd. Length o.a. 481 ft., breadth 62 ft. D.w. tonnage 12,235. One 4-cylinder Doxford engine, 2,850 b.h.p., speed 12 knots. One of many similar ships built before the war. Post-war units of this size usually have their funnel further aft.

The s.s. *British Soldier*, 21,082 tons gross. Built 1954 for the British Tanker Co. Ltd. by John Brown & Co. (Clyde-bank) Ltd. One of six similar ships in the fleet, each of 32,000 tons d.w. and which measure 665 ft. in o.a. length and 85 ft. in breadth. They have ten triple tanks with pump room right forward. Two turbines D.R. geared to a single shaft give an output of 12,500 s.h.p. and a speed of $14\frac{3}{4}$ knots. Distinguish from 28,000-ton type by open base to bridge and position of after kingposts.

Caltex

There are in all over fifty ocean-going tankers bearing the familiar *Caltex* prefix to their names. Most of these are either of T2 design or are new, rather larger vessels. Over a third of them are operated under the Panamanian flag by the Overseas Tankship Corp., New York. Others, under the French and Dutch colours are owned by the Outremer de Nav. Petroliere S.A., Paris, and the N.V. Nederlandsche Pacific Tankvaart Maats, The Hague. Another fleet flies the Red Ensign.

The British flag company of the Caltex group—Overseas Tankship (U.K.) Limited—was incorporated in London in August, 1950. During the first year of its existence the Company owned and operated twelve T2 tankers with a number of others of this type on bareboat charter.

In March, 1952, they took delivery of the first of eleven tankers

The m.s. *Caltex Delhi*, 8,527 tons gross. Built and engined by Wm. Doxford & Sons Ltd. in 1952 for Overseas Tankship (U.K.) Ltd. Length o.a. 490 ft., breadth 62 ft. D.w. capacity 12,350 tons. One 4-cylinder Doxford engine, 5,150 b.h.p., speed 13 knots. One of four sisters.

The s.s. *Caltex Bahrain*, 11,804 tons gross. Built and engined 1953 by Hawthorn Leslie & Co. Ltd. for Overseas Tankship (U.K.) Ltd. Length o.a. 544 ft., breadth 70 ft. D.w. capacity 17,450 tons. Two steam turbines geared to a single shaft, 8,200 s.h.p., speed 15 knots. One of a class of five. Note the permanent awnings over poop accommodation.

ordered from British shipyards. This was the *Caltex Kenya* (12,350 tons deadweight), a Doxford-built motor ship which was joined later that year by the similar *Caltex Tanganyika, Caltex Delhi* and *Caltex Calcutta*—all from the same yard.

In November, 1952, Hawthorn Leslie delivered the turbine-driven *Caltex Liverpool* (17,450 tons deadweight) and a year later the *Caltex Bahrain* and *Caltex Manchester*. This class was rounded off by two Furness-built units, the *Caltex Canberra* and *Caltex Perth*, both of which came out in 1953.

Two slightly larger vessels—of 18,000 tons deadweight—to be named *Caltex Edinburgh* and *Caltex Newcastle* are on order from Scotts and Hawthorn Leslie and are due for delivery in 1956 and 1957.

A fifty per cent. interest in the Caltex group of companies is owned by Texaco, which features on a later page.

Eagle

The Eagle Oil & Shipping Company Ltd. is probably better known in British petroleum circles for the ownership of an important tanker fleet than for the marketing and distribution of Shell petroleum products in South America, whereas in the latter country the reverse applies.

The fleet came into being in 1912, when oil production in Mexico was developing so rapidly that the parent company—the Mexican Eagle Oil Co.—found it necessary to provide transport for its oil to markets in the United Kingdom and South America. The two vessels *San Dunstano* and *San Eduardo*, totalling 18,140 tons deadweight, were the forerunners of the present fleet of Eagle ships, which are all named after Mexican saints or saints closely connected with Mexican tradition. By the outbreak of the war in 1914, a further fourteen ships had been added to the fleet, increasing the total tonnage to 185,000 deadweight.

During both wars Eagle units played an important part. In the first conflict much of the fuel supplied to the Royal Navy came from Mexico in Eagle ships, others of which served as fleet auxiliaries. Five were lost in that and sixteen during the course of the second world war.

With the return to peace the Company set about rebuilding its fleet, commencing with the purchase of three British and two American (T2 type) war-built ships, totalling 76,000 tons deadweight. These were renamed *San Wenceslao*, *San Wilfrido*, *San Virgilio*, *San Leonardo* and *San Leopoldo*. In addition two larger turbo-electric tankers were built in 1949-50, the *San Silvestre* and *San Salvador*, both 16,000 tons deadweight. These were followed by the similar sized but diesel driven *San Patricio* and the 18,000-ton *San Fernando* and *San Florentino*, which had turbines. At the end of 1955 another of this class, the *San Fabian*, was fitting out, while six others were on order. Besides these the Company has contracted for two 31,000-ton and four 32,000-ton tankers. At that date the Eagle fleet totalled twenty large vessels in service, as well as two smaller ones, the coaster *San Castro* and the *San Dario*, which operates on the Thames.

The t.e.s. *San Silvestre*, 10,953 tons gross. The first tanker to be built for the Eagle Oil & Shipping Co. Ltd. after the Second World War and their first to have turbo-electric propulsion. Delivered by the Furness S.B. Co. Ltd. in July, 1949. Length o.a. 537 ft., breadth 69 ft. G.E.C. machinery and two La Mont boilers, 9,000 s.h.p., service speed 14¾ knots. 15,910 tons d.w. Nine tank compartments, eight with three and one with four divisions, the latter being adapted for carrying lubricating oils.

The s.s. *San Florentino*, 12,215 tons gross. The first of the 'F' class ships, all of which have a d.w. tonnage of 18,000 and closely resemble the new Shell general purpose tankers. Built and engined 1953 by Cammell Laird for the Eagle Tanker Co., a newly formed associate of the Eagle Oil & Shipping Co. Length o.a. 556 ft., breadth 69 ft. Two steam turbines D.R. geared to a single shaft. Two La Mont boilers, 500 lb. p.s.i. 800 deg. F., 8,500 s.h.p., speed 14½ knots.

Esso

The fleet of tankers wearing the Esso funnel marking is a vast one and operates under many different flags—American, Belgian, British, Danish, Dutch, French, German, Italian, Panamanian and Venezuelan for ocean-going tonnage, and many more for coastal craft. Typical of new tonnage are the *Esso Paris*, 27,400 tons deadweight, completed in 1954 for the Esso Standard S.A. Francaise, and the *Esso Oxford* of 26,650 tons deadweight, the first of a series of five sisters built for service under the Red Ensign. This class, which also includes the *Esso Cambridge, Esso Exeter, Esso Westminster* and *Esso York,* is designed to carry crude oil from the Persian Gulf and Eastern Mediterranean to the Esso refinery at Fawley, on Southampton Water, and incorporates features not normally seen in British-built ships. These include a bulbous form of bow and the use of

The s.s. *Esso Paris*, 17,378 tons gross. She is the largest of a fleet of nine tankers owned by the Esso Standard S.A., Paris. Built 1954 at St. Nazaire by the Chantiers & Ateliers de St. Nazaire (Penhoet). Length o.a. 628 ft., breadth 83 ft. D.w. tonnage 27,400. D.R. geared turbines 12,500 s.hp., speed 16½ knots. Note the American style stem, raked above and vertical below the waterline.

The s.s. *Esso Oxford*, 17,512 tons gross, one of five sisters built by British yards for the Esso Petroleum Co. Ltd. Completed late 1953 by Cammell Laird & Co. Ltd. Length o.a. 628 ft., breadth 82.5 ft. D.w. capacity 26,650 tons. Single-screw high-pressure turbines. Service speed 16 knots at 16,500 s.h.p. Fitted with bulbous bow. Seen running trials off the Isle of Arran.

high pressure, high temperature steam. The turbines, operating at 850 p.s.i. and 850 degrees F., give a service speed of 16 knots. Each ship has ten sets of tanks (thirty in all), with the two pumprooms situated at the extreme ends of the cargo space. The rotary pumping equipment is such that the vessels can load at 5,000 tons per hour and discharge at 3,000 tons per hour.

Also owned in Great Britain are a number of T2 standard type tankers, a few remaining diesel driven, war-built vessels and several of pre-war construction. This fleet is now in a period of transition and to replace old units six tankers of 36,000 tons deadweight have been ordered, two from the Tyne and the others from Germany, for delivery in 1957-58.

Latterly some of the more elderly ocean-going tankers have been employed to distribute oil from Fawley to the main Esso depots around the British Isles—Purfleet, Bowling, the Mersey, Hull, Avonmouth, etc. From these points further distribution to outlying ports such as Aberdeen, Preston, etc., is done by small coastal units, while barges are used for inland work.

THE WORLD'S TANKERS

The m.s. *Tynefield*.
12,238 tons gross, 18,000 tons d.w.
Built 1952.

The m.s. *Avonfield*.
11,310 tons gross, 16,500 tons d.w.
Built 1953.

The m.s. *Wheatfield*.
10,646 tons gross, 16,300 tons d.w.
Built 1952.

The m.s. *Duffield*.
10.201 tons gross, 14,500 tons d.w.
Built 1952.

The m.s. *Pontfield*.
8,319 tons gross, 12,800 tons d.w.
Built 1939.

The m.s. *Laganfield*.
8,196 tons gross, 12,472 tons d.w.
Built 1950.

The m.s. *Redefield*.
786 tons gross, 1,034 tons d.w.
Built 1940.

Hunting

The firm of Hunting & Son Ltd., whose present tanker fleet is the largest independently owned in Great Britain, was formed in 1874. They first became tanker owners in 1893 when their then newly formed Northern Petroleum Tank S.S. Co. Ltd. took delivery of the *Duffield*, a ship of 5,000 tons deadweight and of a design very similar to that of their *Saxoleine*, which is illustrated on page 30. During the early part of this century Huntings also owned some general cargo ships, but few of these survived the 1914-18 war.

Of the company's bygone vessels the most notable was the first *Gretafield*, a tanker of 10,191 tons gross, which at the time of her construction in 1928 was one of the largest to be owned in the U.K. Losses during the second world war were heavy, and to offset these a number of war-built standard type tankers were built or purchased, amongst them two American-built T2's.

A little later the company initiated a large building programme, ordering a number of 12,000/18,000-tonners. An interesting feature of these was that no two were of the same design. The first to be ready was the m.s. *Laganfield*, 12,472 tons deadweight, which was delivered in December, 1950. The tenth and last of these, the *Forthfield*, a turbine-driven vessel of about 18,000 tons deadweight, was delivered by Hawthorn Leslie in May, 1955.

At the close of that year the Hunting fleet comprised twelve large tankers and one coastal unit, the m.s. *Redefield*, of 1,034 tons deadweight. Besides these there was still one turbine-driven tanker of 31,000 tons deadweight on order from Hawthorn Leslie, but not due for launching until 1956-57.

The m.s. *Huntfield*, 11,113 tons gross, built 1954. Length o.a. 529 ft., breadth 70 ft. D.w. tonnage 16,500. Speed on trials 15 knots. Note the unusual arrangement of the poop, open below at its forward end.

The Niarchos Group

One of the outstanding achievements of recent years has been the creation by Mr. Stavros S. Niarchos of what is now probably the world's largest independent tanker fleet. It was in the 'thirties that he first started buying dry-cargo ships for his own account, then some tanker tonnage: subsequently he detached himself from the family milling business, in which he had held a prominent position.

Heavy war losses to his fleet were offset by the acquisition of war-built tonnage, while in 1947 he initiated his great tanker building programme by ordering the *World Peace*, 18,000 tons deadweight, from the Bethlehem Sparrows Point shipyard. At the time of writing, eight years later, the fleets of *World* and *Saxon* tankers alone total over twenty units, of which over one half have a deadweight capacity exceeding 30,000 tons apiece.

The eight *Saxon* tankers comprise four British-, two Dutch- and two Swedish-built units, all turbine-driven craft of over 20,000 tons deadweight. Of the *World* tankers, all but the first two, the U.S.-built *World Peace* and *World Liberty*, have capacities exceeding 32,000 tons, while the *World Glory* is of 45,509 tons. Their largest unit, the *Spyros Niarchos*, 47,750 tons deadweight, was launched by Vickers-Armstrongs, Barrow, in December, 1955, while a similar vessel is to follow. Besides smaller ships the Group has two tankers each of 38,870 tons deadweight on order in Sweden and eight of 40,500 tons deadweight from Japanese yards.

Amongst the principal companies of the Niarchos Group are the Imperial Shipping Investment Co. of Bermuda, which manages the vessels, the World Tankers Corporation of Liberia, World Tankers Inc. of Panama, the Oriental Tanker Corporation S.A., the International Transport Corporation, the Cia. International de Vapores S.A. and the Intermarine Navigation Corporation, the Neptune Tanker Corporation and the Mercury Tanker Corporation.

The s.s. *World Concord*, second of a group of four ships, each of 20,000 tons gross, which were built 1952-3-4 by Vickers Armstrongs for the Niarchos Group. The first pair, which came from the builders' Barrow establishment, were the *World Unity* and *World Concord*, which had a d.w. capacity of approximately 32,500 tons, an overall length of 653 ft. and a breadth of 86 ft. The later Tyne-built vessels *World Enterprise* and *World Harmony* were 10 ft. longer and carried an extra 500 tons. All four are turbine driven and have a sea speed of 15 knots.

Illustration on page 157

The s.s. *Saxonglen*, 13,321 tons gross. Built 1953 by Vickers Armstrongs Ltd., Newcastle, for Imperial Shipping Investment Co., Hamilton, Bermuda, one of the Niarchos Group of companies. Length o.a. 536 ft., breadth 75 ft. D.w. capacity 20,433 tons, Nine triple tanks. D.R. geared turbines, 8,300 s.h.p., speed 14½ knots Sisters: *Saxondale*, *Saxonglade*. *Saxonmead*.

The s.s. *World Justice*, 20,235 tons gross. Built 1954 for the Niarchos Group by the Mitsui Zosen K.K., Nagasaki. Length o.a. 660 ft., breadth 88 ft. 32,551 tons d.w. Ten triple tanks. D.R. geared turbines. Steam 600 p.s.i. 850 deg. F. Speed on load trials 17.66 knots. Sister: *World Jury*, built 1955.

The s.s. *Regent Hawk*, 8,169 tons gross, which was built by Swan, Hunter, & Wigham Richardson in 1946. Length o.a. 485 ft., breadth 59 ft., 12,180 tons d.w. Triple expansion engines, speed 11 knots

Regent

The fleet owned by Trinidad Leaseholds Ltd. and its associate, the Regent Oil Co. Ltd., though not numerically large is of considerable interest. The two largest units are owned by the former, these being the *Regent Hawk* and *Regent Royal,* of approximately 12,000 and 15,000 tons deadweight respectively. The former, laid down as a standard ship, was completed in 1945 to her present owners' requirements. The launch of the *Regent Royal* on January 18th, 1954, was a notable occasion, for the christening ceremony was performed by the Princess Royal. This was a sequel to an earlier royal trip to the West Indies in the *Regent Springbok,* a tanker time-chartered by Trinidad Leaseholds.

These two units operate on a regular haul, bringing spirit from the company's refinery at Pointe-a-Pierre, Trinidad, to U.K. depots, such as Immingham, Canvey Island, Avonmouth, Dingle and Grangemouth. Smaller quantities of lubricating oil are also brought to Britain. Coastwise distribution of Regent petrol is mostly done by Rowbotham coastal tankers, although the Regent Oil Co. Ltd. owns a fleet of small vessels. These are headed by the m.s. *Regent Jane,* 376 tons gross, which operates mostly on the west coast of England. The rest of their fleet, all of which bear the prefix *Regent,* consists of motor-driven tank lighters, which are chiefly used for inland distribution—up the River Severn, etc.—to depots such as Stour-port. Some of these little vessels are also used in the Bristol Channel area, with Swansea as their western limit.

The m.s. *Regent Royal*, 10,024 tons gross. Delivered to Trinidad Leaseholds Ltd. in May, 1954, by the Blythswood S.B. Co. Ltd. Length 514 ft. o.a., breadth 65.5 ft. 15,000 tons d.w. on 25 ft. 3 in. draught. One 4-cylinder Doxford type engine, 4,500 b.h.p. Loaded trial speed 14·6 knots.

The s.s. *Vexilla*, 20,749 tons gross. Built and engined by Cammell Laird, she was delivered to Shell on 17th August, 1955. The second of a group of twelve, each of 31,000 tons d.w., she has an overall length of 660 ft. and a moulded breadth of 84 ft. 3 in. Geared turbines give a service speed of 16½ knots. The ten main cargo tanks are divided by the usual two longitudinal bulkheads, but these are arranged to make the centre tanks considerably wider than is usual. Of the side tanks six are used for water ballast only. Until the completion of the 'Z' class the *Vexilla* and her sisters are the largest owned by Shell.

Shell

At the close of 1955 and excluding small vessels the Shell fleet totalled over 460 units with a combined deadweight tonnage of 7 millions. Of these over 200 were owned, the rest—representing some 4½ million tons deadweight—being on charter.

Their tanker *Auris*, famed as the first merchant ship to be fitted with a gas turbine, will continue to be used as a floating test-bed. During 1956 she is to be stripped of her existing machinery, which comprises one 1,200 h.p. B.T.H. gas turbine, three diesel generators and electrical transmission, and be fitted instead with a single gas turbine of 5,500 h.p. which will use direct gearing to a fixed bladed propeller.

In 1951 Shell placed orders for seventy ships and the last of these are scheduled for completion by 1957. Amongst vessels of this programme now being delivered are various of the fifty 18,000-ton (deadweight) turbine-driven general purpose tankers and of the twelve 31,000-tonners. Of the latter the first two, the French-built *Isanda* and the British *Vexilla* entered

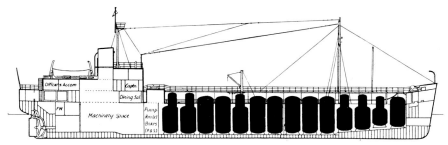

A section through the s.s. *Butagaz*, showing the arrangement of the liquid gas carrying cylinders which are arranged in three rows. The vessel—built in a dry dock—was floated out on 28th June, 1955, and replaces the *Alberta*, lost during the war. She has an overall length of 279 ft. and a moulded breadth of 39 ft. 5 in. She was constructed by Chantiers Naval de la Ciotat for Societe Shell d'Algerie to operate between the Shell refinery at Berre, near Marseilles, and North African ports. Singe-screw triple-expansion engines of 1,350 s.h.p. give a service speed of 11 knots.

service in the late summer of 1955. At present these are the largest ships to be owned by Shell, but under the same programme two, each of 38,000 tons deadweight, were ordered, the *Zaphon* and *Zenatia*, from Swan, Hunter, & Wigham Richardson and Cammell Laird respectively.

In the autumn of 1955 another large building programme was announced. This covered over forty ships, some of them of the familiar 18,000-ton general purpose type and the rest of a new design with a carrying capacity of 32,000 tons.

The s.s. *Hemifusis*, 12,182 tons gross, one of a series of fifty general purpose tankers for the Shell fleet. Built 1954 by Cammell Laird & Co. Ltd. Length o.a. 556 ft., breadth 69 ft. D.R. geared turbines, 8,250 b.h.p. speed 14½ knots. Note the addition of an extra deck aft, a new feature for Shell tankers.

Texaco

The origins of The Texas Company, now one of the largest of United States oil concerns, date back to 1901, when an oil well—the Lucas gusher—roared into life on Spindletop Hill, near Beaumont, Texas. Then two men, Joseph Cullinan, long experienced in the oil business, and Arnold Schlaet, a financier, formed the Texas Fuel Company with a capital of $ 50,000.

The richness of this field brought some two hundred other oil firms into being, and with local oil prices dropping to a mere few cents a barrel, the problem was soon not one of production, but of transportation and marketing. Backed by experience Cullinan contracted to buy in bulk, and laid a twenty-mile pipeline to deep water, where it could be shipped for profitable marketing. By 1905, thanks to his personality and drive, he had not only developed a good home market, but was also invading the European one. The original tiny concern was soon outgrown and in August, 1902, the present Texas Company was registered, its capital being $ 1,000,000. Other successful wells in S. Texas, Louisiana and Oklahoma assured plentiful supplies of crude and the first refinery was built at Port Arthur, some twenty miles from Spindletop. This was followed by the purchase of some barges and a tanker, and the building of a 473-mile pipeline from Oklahoma to the Gulf Coast, the latter a bold venture which paid off.

Today Texaco (the trade name originated in a cable address) has oil interests throughout most of the free world and a 50 per cent. holding in the Caltex group of companies, which though again world-wide, are particularly concerned with Eastern markets. A 30 per cent. interest is also held in the Arabian American Oil Company (Aramco) which operates in Saudi Arabia and in the Trans-Arabian Pipe Line Company, which moves oil from Saudi Arabia to Sidon in Lebanon.

The Company's American flag ships total twenty-three, and are chiefly employed between the Gulf of Mexico and U.S. Atlantic ports, and to a lesser extent, along the Pacific Coast. Those under the Panamanian flag include one small Caribbean tanker and four large vessels which bring crude from the Middle East to the United States or Canada. A further nine—all motor tankers—operate under Norwegian colours.

The s.s. *Texas*, 17,892 tons gross, is one of four sister ships owned by the Texas Company (Panama) Inc. which are normally employed in transporting crude oil from the Middle East to the U.S.A. and Canada. Built 1949 by the Bethlehem Steel Co., Quincy, she has a d.w. capacity of 28,081 tons, an overall length of 624 ft. and a breadth of 84 ft. Geared turbines give a speed of 16 knots. The others in this class are named *Kentucky*, *Ohio* and *Pennsylvania*. Four further vessels are now on order or under construction in Europe.

The s.s. *New York*, 12,789 tons gross, is one of a group of four built at Newport News in 1949 for The Texas Company, the others being named *California*, *Connecticut* and *North Dakota*. The largest of the Company's ships to fly the American flag, they have a d.w. capacity of 19,153/19,203 tons, an overall length of 565 ft. and a breadth of 72 ft. Geared turbines give a sustained sea speed of over 18 knots. Also under the American flag are five of 14,000 tons d.w., fourteen of the T2 type (16,000 tons), and two smaller vessels, one of which is employed on the Great Lakes.

Some Other Present-Day Tanker Fleets

The following photographs show units of yet other tanker fleets owned in America and in Norway, Denmark, Sweden, France and Japan. As previously stated, there are so many individual tanker-owning firms in existence that it is impossible to include more than a representative few. A study of these pages emphasizes how international is the approach to tanker design; that despite difference in nationality most of the vessels shown are of generally similar layout, yet owing to variation in detail they differ appreciably in appearance.

The *W. Alton Jones*, 22,757 tons gross, is one of the four super-tankers which comprise the fleet of Grand Bassa Tankers Inc. This firm is a subsidiary of Cities Service Oil Company, New York, which itself has a fleet of eleven tankers—one T3 and ten T2 type—and has three 32,500-ton d.w. American flag vessels on order. The *W. Alton Jones* is named after the chairman of Cities Service, while the other three, *Statue of Liberty*, *Cradle of Liberty* and *Liberty Bell*, bear names symbolical of the cities of New York, Boston and Philadelphia. The four ships were built in 1954 by the Newport News S.B. & D.D. Co. and are designed for the Persian Gulf-River Delaware run. They have a length o.a. of 707 ft., a breadth mld. of 93 ft. and a d.w. capacity of 38,900 tons. The fastest and most powerful super-tankers yet built in the States, their turbines develop a normal s.h.p. of 20,000. Speed 17½ knots.

The s.s. *Las Piedras*, 18,611 tons gross, of the Afran Transport Co., Monrovia, was delivered in January, 1953, by the Bethlehem Sparrows Point shipyard. She is one of eight generally similar vessels in this fleet, of which six are American and two British built. The Afran Transport Co. is a subsidiary of the Gulf Oil Corporation, New York, who under their own name possess a fleet of some forty ocean-going tankers. Length o.a. 645 ft., breadth 84 ft. D.R. geared turbines, 13,750 s.h.p,. speed 16¼ knots.

The *Amoco New York*, 10,414 tons gross, is one of a fleet of twelve owned by the American Oil Company, New York. Built as the *Brandy Station* by the Sun S.B. & D.D. Co. in 1943, she was later renamed *Pan New York* and was known as this until 1955. A turbo-electric ship of modified T2 design, she has thirty tanks instead of the usual twenty-six. She can lift 7,000 tons of hot asphalt in addition to bunker fuel or other black oil. The asphalt is carried in eight centre tanks and maintained at a temperature of 325 degrees. Length o.a. 523 ft. 6 in., breadth 68 ft. 16,785 tons d.w. Speed 14½ knots.

The *P. C. Spencer*, 16,153 tons gross, is one of a group of three owned by Petroleum Tankers Inc., a subsidiary of the Sinclair Refining Co. Inc., New York. They are the largest units in the combined fleet, which totals over a dozen vessels, another of which, the *Flagship Sinco*, is shown on an earlier page. The *P. C. Spencer* has an o.a. length of 604 ft. 7 in. and a mld. breadth of 78 ft. D.R. geared turbines developing 13,750 s.h.p. give a speed of 17 knots. She and the *M. L. Gosney* were built in 1953, the *W. P. Thirtle* in 1955, all by the Bethlehem Sparrows Point shipyard.

The s.s. *Socony Vacuum*, 17,444 tons gross, flag ship of the Socony Mobil Oil Company, Inc., New York, built by Bethlehem, Quincy, in 1954. Socony Mobil owns fifteen vessels of a total deadweight of 266,223 tons, under the U.S. flag. Associated companies include six tankers owned by the Brilliant Transportation Company, S.A., under the Panamanian flag, of which s.s. *Waneta* and s.s. *Wapello* are post-war super-tankers. The British company, Mobil Transportation Co. Ltd., owns the s.s. *Royal Arrow* and the s.s. *Sylvan Arrow*, both built 1954/55, and of super-tanker type. Mobil Oil Francaise (Societe Anonyme Mazout Transports) own three ships, of which the s.s. *Aramis* and s.s. *Porthos* are modern super-tankers. The German flag fleet (Mobil Oil A.G.) consists of two ships, one pre-war and one post-war.

The *Stanvac South Africa*, 17,407 tons gross, is one of a class of three ships, the largest to be owned by the Standard Vacuum Group, who operate several fleets of tankers under the American, British, Dutch and Panamanian flags. The *Stanvac South Africa* and *Stanvac Japan* were built in 1953 by the Mitsubishi Shipbuilding and Engineering Co. Ltd. and were joined the following year by the Cammell Laird-built *Stanvac India*. They have a d.w. capacity of 26,500 tons on an o.a. length of 628 ft.

The *Western Sun*, 18,810 tons gross, is the flagship of the Sun Oil Co., Philadelphia, whose fleet totals over twenty tankers. Built by the Sun S.B. & D.D. Co. in 1954, she has an o.a. length of 641 ft. and a breadth of 84 ft. 5 in. Two sets of Westinghouse D.R. geared turbines give a speed of 16½ knots.

The *Orion Planet*, 18,717 tons gross, and her sister *Orion Clipper* were built in 1954 for Tankers Joint Venture by the Bethlehem Steel Co.'s Sparrows Point shipyard. Of 29,400 tons d.w., they have an o.a. length of 644 ft. and a breadth of 84 ft. Geared turbines give a speed of 17 knots. Two others in this class, the *Orion Comet* and *Orion Star*, owned by Oil Carriers Joint Venture, were built in 1953 by the Bethlehem Steel Co. at Quincy. All four are managed by the Orion Shipping & Trading Co. Inc.

The Norwegian m.t. *Bergeboss*, 20,448 tons gross, is owned by Sigval Bergesen d/y & Co., Stavanger. Built by Eriksbergs M.V. in 1954, she was notable in being the largest vessel yet from a Swedish shipyard, while her sister *Bergeland* (by Rosenberg M.V., 1954) was similarly the largest from a Norwegian one. The *Bergeboss* has a d.w. capacity of 32,900 tons and is twin-screw. Also in the 'Berge' fleet are four motor tankers of 16,000/18,000 tons d.w. and the new *Bergehuss*, 33,000 tons d.w.

The Norwegian m.t. *Gunnar Knudsen* has a gross tonnage of 11,023 and was built by Gotaverken in 1954 to the order of A/S Borgestad (Gunnar Knudsen). A vessel of 17,420 tons d.w., she has an o.a. length of 550 ft. and a breadth mld. of 66 ft. A 9-cylinder Gotaverken diesel engine gives a speed of 14½ knots. She is the fourth tanker built since the war for these owners. The Caltex funnel marking which she bears is a reminder that Scandinavian tankers are almost invariably built for charter work.

The Norwegian *Polarsol*, seen leaving Fawley, is a motor tanker of 10,022 tons gross. Owned by the Polaris Whaling Co. (Melsom & Melsom), of Nanset. She was built by Barclay Curle & Co. in 1939. She is typical of a number of Norwegian tankers which are used each season to take out oil fuel and other supplies to the Antarctic whaling fleet and bring back whale oil, but which rely for the rest of the year on normal charter work.

The Danish m.t. *Tove Maersk*, 8,453 tons gross, is one of the newer but smaller sized tankers owned by the several companies headed by A. P. Moller, of Copenhagen. A vessel 9f 13,160 tons d.w., she was built in Belgium, 1954, by Jos. Boel & Sons, Tamise. She has an o.a. length of 479 ft. and a breadth of 63 ft. One 6-cylinder B. & W. engine of 5,375 b.h.p. gives a service speed of 14 knots. Note the deck recess made necessary by the lowered placing of the gravity davits. The Moller fleet, over sixty strong, is one of Denmark's largest. In it tankers feature most prominently, then cargo liners, fruiters and short sea traders.

The Swedish m.t. *Oceanus*, 16,155 tons gross, owned by the Johnson Line (Rederi A/B Nordstjernan), Stockholm, is notable in being the first really large tanker to have her bridge and all accommodation aft, although this layout was adopted for the much smaller *Brunswick*, *Permian* and *Winkler* of the early 'thirties. Built at Gothenburg, 1954, by the Lindholmens Varv., the *Oceanus* has a d.w. capacity of 24,500 tons, a length o.a. of 610 ft. 10 in. and a breadth of 75 ft. 10 in. Two 9-cylinder Gotaverken type engines give a speed of $14\frac{1}{2}$ knots. The Johnson Line is famed for its very fine fleet of over thirty cargo liners and apart from some very small coastal vessels the *Oceanus* is their only tanker.

The French m.t. *Champagne*, 11,045 tons gross, is one of a fleet of some sixteen tankers—almost all diesel driven—owned by the Societe Francaise de Transports Petroliers (S.F.T.P.), Paris. The first of two sisters of 16,900 tons d.w., she and the *Roussillon* were built 1950-1 by the Ateliers et Chantiers de la Seine Maritime, Le Trait, and as is often the custom in France, was launched in a complete state. She has an o.a. length of 541 ft. 8 in. and a breadth of 70 ft. 4 in. and is propelled by an 8-cylinder B. & W. type diesel engine which gives a speed of 13 knots.

The Japanese *Daikyo Maru*, 13,224 tons gross, was delivered in August, 1953, by the Harima Shipbuilding & Engineering Co. Ltd., Aioi, to the Daikyo Oil Co. Ltd., Tokyo, whose only ship she is. With an o.a. length of 580 ft. 6 in. and a breadth of 73 ft. she has a d.w. capacity of 20,861 tons. Geared turbines designed for a maximum continuous output of 9,000 s.h.p. give a service speed of 15 knots. Like most modern Japanese tankers, she has a very pleasing yet orthodox profile.

Index of Ships

NOTE: The use of heavy type numerals denotes illustration, of ship or sister, under present or previous name.

MERCHANT SHIPS : WORLD BUILT

THIS comprehensive illustrated Register of new ships is published annually, presenting each year particulars of every new merchant ship of 1,000 tons gross and upwards delivered in the previous twelve months from the shipyards of the major shipbuilding countries of the world.

The volume opens with an introduction by A. C. Hardy, B.SC., M.I.N.A., which is followed by a summary of the world's shipbuilding with statistics and an analysis of new ships under the names of owners and managers. The shipbuilding activities of each country are then considered under separate sections: Great Britain and Northern Ireland, America, Australia, Belgium, Canada, Denmark, Finland, France, Germany, Italy, Japan, Netherlands, Norway, Portugal, Spain, Sweden and others. Each of these sections has an introduction summarising the shipbuilding activities of the country, showing the output of every shipyard, type of ship delivered, gross tonnage, and whether for home or export market. These sections are liberally illustrated by photographs or designs of the principal new ships, tankers, passenger vessels, dry cargo ships, bulk carriers, coasters, ferries, and specialised types of every kind.

Finally there is the International Alphabetical Register compiled from authoritative sources, which gives particulars of ownership, tonnages, dimensions, propelling machinery and speed of each new ship of the year.

FROM THE PRESS REVIEWS

". . . extended to include photographs and details of foreign built vessels . . . This extension of the book's scope undoubtedly makes it the more valuable by affording the reader the opportunity of comparing design trends apparent in British and foreign built tonnage . . . French and German translations of the section describing the book's arrangement . . . it is a reasonably priced book of undoubted value and no one whose business or hobby is ships should be without a shelf prepared to receive its new 'Merchant Ships' each year." *Lloyds List and Shipping Register*

"The book affords a splendid example of what enterprise can achieve." *Fairplay*

"In three years of publication this book has set a high standard of accuracy and interest, well maintained in the latest issue. The annual issues form an invaluable reference series, the illustrations and plans being of particular merit." *The Navy*

"The publishers are to be congratulated on the improved arrangement of the third volume in a series . . . The whole provides an extremely useful and attractive record of the world's merchant shipbuilding output." *Shipping World*

". . . outstanding for the large number of ship photographs and plans it contains —not elsewhere available in such a compact publication." *Liverpool Journal of Commerce*

"Well established as an essential reference book for all who wish to keep up-to-date on the features of new ships of all classes." *Merchant Navy Journal*

"Most conveniently the new ships are listed under their country of building, the builders of each nation who have contributed (and the name of their contribution) being appropriately tabulated." *Shipbuilder and Shipping Record*

"The volume should prove of the greatest interest and value, not only to those engaged in the shipbuilding, marine engineering and shipping industries, but to all who are in any way interested in the merchant ships of the world." *Marine News*

". . . now the format has taken on its final shape, these books will become a standard reference for the future." *Seafarer*

Full particulars will be sent on request.

ADLARD COLES LTD.
7 BRUNSWICK PLACE, SOUTHAMPTON, ENGLAND

JOHN DE GRAFF INC.
31 EAST 10TH STREET, NEW YORK, 3, N.Y., U.S.A.